HEALING HERBS

OF THE UPPER RÍO GRANDE

To my mother
    who loved me
To Mary Austin
    who was my friend
I dedicate
    this book

L. S. M. C.

Médica of the
Río Grande Valley

HEALING

OF THE UPPER

L S M CURTIN

Drawings by P G Napolitano

LABORATORY OF

SANTA FÉ

HERBS
RÍO GRANDE

ANTHROPOLOGY
NEW MEXICO

Cacti of the Río Grande

•CONTENTS

MAIN LIBRARY

SAN FRANCISCO PUBLIC LIBRARY

By Way of Preface

Anthropology being the science—or the study—of man, a very desirable end, obviously, is that of making the study just as complete as possible. Every representative facet of man's life, present as well as past, deserves attention because accurate information, properly sorted and interpreted, gives us the whole story of man.

It is just as important to know about plant-medicine as about arrowheads or papyrus manuscripts—and it is important to know about those two activities of man, make no mistake about that! There was plant-medicine before legendary Æsculapius or Hippocrates, long before Pasteur and Lister. In wholly civilized areas it became one of the parents of the medical profession, in less cultural surroundings it persists as an independent activity, vastly important. The wise and gen-

1

erally unlettered practicioner of this folk-healing must be studied along with the simples and the remedies—half medical truths and half mendicant magic. The living herbalist is an important link with the medicine-man of long-forgotten cave-dwelling ancestors—ours, no less. We must study the present in the light of the past.

Not the least important result of applying that concept in this book is the significant relationship which the text establishes between the plant-medicine of the United States Southwest and that of distant Morocco. The Southwest, of course, became a Spanish colony only a few generations after the Moorish hold upon most of Spain was broken, in 1492. A clever and an exceedingly accomplished folk, they left, as a result of the centuries of their occupation, a stamp of cultural contact upon Spain which is indelible to this day. So, like many another part of Hispanic America, the Southwest felt the direct and the indirect influences of that Moorish occupation of the homeland: direct, in the persons of Moorish artisans, Moorish architects, and Moorish servants, who accompanied the *conquistadores* and their successors to the New World; indirect, in the infusion of Moorish customs, words, and knowledge which every venturesome Spaniard brought to the Americas.

In pointing up, within its own specialized field, the importance of the Moors in this hemisphere, this book underlines the urgent need for a thoroughgoing study of Moorish influence throughout the three Americas during the colonial period. There is a deal more of it than the average student realizes.

L. S. M. Curtin has made a valuable contribution to cultural anthropology in this book. It is a gift of considerable worth too, to the pharmacopœia. Paul C. Standley, the distinguished Curator of the Herbarium of the Chicago Natural History Museum, feels that this work is "well prepared", that it contains "a large amount of unique information"; Standley adds:

2

"Very little ever has been done in the field of ethnobotany in New Mexico, so that every addition to knowledge of the subject is bound to have importance from the standpoint of folklore, and quite possibly also in a practical way. The information is some of it of ancient origin and, in spite of the natural conservatism of the Spanish-speaking people, it is bound to be lost with the rapidly changing conditions of present times. Probably some of the data that Mrs. Curtin has assembled can no longer be obtained. I believe that the publication of this manuscript will serve a very definite purpose, and be a worth-while contribution to botanical science."

About fifteen years ago I edited an important manuscript which I then took through the throes of publication—"The Ethno-Botany of the Maya", by Ralph L. Roys. Throughout a long series of editing other scientific publications, I never got over the feeling that to work on the Roys plant-remedy book was a privilege for which I should be grateful. I have done the same sort of work on the Curtin study . . . and I have emerged with the same conviction. I am grateful for it.

MAURICE RIES

Director

LABORATORY OF ANTHROPOLOGY

ACKNOWLEDGMENT

It was Mary Austin's anxiety over the rapid decline of folk experience into ultimate discard and consequent oblivion that inspired me to undertake this work. With her encouragement and my natural enthusiasm for the subject, I began to collect local remedies as well as the plants used in their composition.

Since a publication of this nature would be valuable only if the plants in question were identified completely, I turned to Paul C. Standley, co-author of "Flora of New Mexico", and at present Curator of the Herbarium, Chicago Natural History Museum. Mr. Standley's extensive work in botany has made him an eminent authority and I acknowledge my deep obligation to him for scientific data. Not only are the original herbarium specimens held by the Chicago Natural History Museum, but duplicates are deposited at the Laboratory of Anthropology, in Santa Fé, where researchers can consult the collection.

With the passing of time came changes in botanical nomenclature, and I appealed to Mr. Standley, who recommended Curator of Botany Joseph Ewan at the University of Colorado

Museum, Boulder, Colorado, to make the necessary corrections. This he consented to undertake with the aid of his wife, Nesta Dunn Ewan, who was trained in botany at the University of California at Los Angeles. The young couple made numerous valuable suggestions which have been followed and the more modern appellation adopted.

I am grateful to Dr. J. P. Harrington of the Bureau of Ethnology, Smithsonian Institution, for proposing Morocco as a valuable source of herbal comparisons and etymologies, and at his instigation I collected material there which has enriched this book. The Moroccan specimens, which were identified by Mr. C. V. Morton, have been left with the Smithsonian Institution.

From the inception of the work, Dr. Frederick Webb Hodge, Director, The Southwest Museum, Los Angeles, and the late Dr. Edgar L. Hewett, of the Museum of New Mexico, Santa Fé, stimulated me with kindly advice and practical aid.

For assistance in the detailed pressing, arrangement, and marking of specimens I am indebted to the late Sheldon Parsons. I am indebted, too, to my daughter, Leonora Paloheimo, who has reviewed and revised the manuscript and who has sustained me with her consistent enthusiasm.

The suggestions of these friendly people, together with my field notes, now formed enough for at least one volume, and although the pleasures of independent research and the limitless opportunity for additional material still beckoned me, I knew it was time to present the results. Consequently, I turned to John Parkinson Keyes, a Harvard graduate and student at London University, for help. He spent a year preparing and rewriting my notes for publication, assorting references, compiling indices, and, in fact, acting as my collaborator to the end that this book was brought into being.

L. S. M. C.

FOREWORD

The fact that the herbalism of our Southwest included, in its modes, all the approaches of the pre-botanical eras makes it the most interesting section of the United States botanically, and therefore the most worthy, to my mind, of serious study. Here is, first of all, the tribal approach in which there is free play of the experimental method of discovery; there is also the folk method which consists of tradition explicitly touched by the early phases of the doctrine of signatures, marked by racial crossings and migrations, such as included the intrusion of Moorish practice transferred to Spain and from Spain to America, with overlappings of traditional Indian, Spanish, and Moorish lore. By such migrations the reach of botanical experience has been expanded not only by extensions of the known field, but also by the substitutions of one familiar remedy for another which in another environment it greatly resembled, and the crossings of mingling traditions.

From the first I had been extremely eager to collect and record the current herbal utilities, but, unfortunately, owing to the crowded condition of my schedule—which involves me most of the time with four or five books on assorted subjects—I had never been able to give myself to that work. Then I had the good fortune to encounter Mrs. Curtin, who was interested, and who possessed, in addition, the intelligence and skill to make a success of such a study; and so I quite happily wished upon her the undertaking of a work on the current herbal practice among the Spanish-speaking natives of New Mexico, compounded of the knowledge of the local Indian lore with extensive detours into the old Spanish and Moorish practices which they had brought with them out of their ancestral experience.

Mrs. Curtin was not only already familiar with Spanish folk practice in New Mexico, and quite willing to put herself to the discipline of acquainting herself with precise botanical knowledge, but was also on such friendly terms with the local Indian tribes as to make it easily possible to include such exchanges as the Spanish natives had made with them in herbal lore. What is here presented is compiled in a fashion which, while it keeps all the folk quality, omits nothing of the truly scientific study. In it will be found the native Spanish practice, enlarged with traditional lore brought out of Moorish contacts, added to by Indian exchanges and altered by the indubitable folk practice of attaching old, familiar, remedial uses to the next nearest thing discovered in the unfamiliar environment of New Mexico. A number of these transitions and crossings are properly indicated in Mrs. Curtin's method of recording.

While we can not certify that all of the remedies described are valid as given, we are at least certain that they are believed to be, among the people who use them. Some of them, we have experimental knowledge, splendidly met the exigencies of human needs; *oshá,* for example, is known to have long been a universal remedy and dependable articles of primitive barter up and down the Río Grande district, and *orégano* has given an equal term of service as a savory herb. Such plants as we find in use, for which we have not been able to detect any genuine service, we more or less suspect have become local substitutes for something closely resembling them in old Spain or northern Africa. Among plants which are used as dyes, we find local examples employed perhaps as far back as five thousand years.

It must also be borne in mind that the knowledge of most of the really reliable and curative drugs known to mankind has come through the experiences of tribes still in purely primitive states; ipecac, cascara, cocaine, quinine, opium, rhubarb, tobacco, sodium-bicarbonate, and the use of these things transcends our acquaintance of the times in which they came into human experience.

It is not only starch and sugar and fats that plants store up, but unequivocal responses to our possible bodily emergencies: for fever, for ænemia, for constipation, for the assaults of malaria and toxic poisonings. I would have you notice, in the lists appended to this work, how many plants respond to costive conditions and mechanical disorders of the digestive tract.

As far back in time as we can go intelligently, what comes to us directly out of such studies as this is an assurance of the extraordinarily free response to human needs from the created universe. So widely spread are the practical and remedial uses of plants that it is not possible to resist the suggestion that there may be just as many plants about us whose latent and unsuspected remedial powers are as valuable as those already discovered. It is with this possibility in view that the author has given herself to the labor of collating and describing those whose uses have already been guessed at by the simple and unsophisticated peoples of our Southwestern borders. It is to Mrs. Curtin, on whose hands has devolved the work of recording this study of our local herbs, that the credit rests for any such hints and suggestions as may be discovered. Most of the cures herein described have been drawn out of a still active and extraordinarily busy practice of herbalism among our local folk groups. Seeing the many good things that have come into our *materia medica* out of such practice in the past, it is not incredible to suppose that there may be still remedial benefits to be discovered in them. It has been, at the least, an absorbingly interesting task to record these early convictions of appreciable good in the herbs of the field that have come under racial attention, before our primary knowledge of them is completely lost.

MARY AUSTIN

INTRODUCTION

The Spanish people of New Mexico live on the soil; they live simply and they have long memories. They can remember the language of Spain three hundred years ago and they have not yet forgotten the ways and customs of those times. Schools, American public schools, have come only recently to their valleys, and the gifts of industry, transportation, and science are not yet necessities in their daily existence. They are a people accustomed to the harvest of their yearly nourishment from the earth, from the fields about their homes, and it is without strangeness that they also draw medicines from the same source. The ever-present earth supplies the needs of its children here, as elsewhere; it is the grocer and the druggist for those who belong to the earth.

A knowledge of the earth's simples is not restricted to the few but lives in the consciousness of all. Any mother may walk forth and gather healing herbs for a sick child, or she may call a neighboring *médica* who will administer the same remedies, adding, perhaps, others from her store. They will all be safe

11

and they will surely cure; or, if not, the child will die . . . *"Que se haga la voluntad de Dios"* (God's will be done). He has given us the plants of the mountains, of the plains and of the fields so that we might help ourselves—perhaps if we knew them *all,* we should never suffer".

Faith and fatalism are the first ingredients in folk medicine; under these is the tradition of properties, and the trail of tradition is sometimes long and winding. Here, for example, is *alfilerillo* (filaree), brought from across the seas with its Moorish name, growing wild as a native weed but treasured still for its helpful attributes. From México, too, have come names and uses learned from the Aztec, and not a little knowledge has accrued from a long and friendly intercourse with the local Pueblo Indians. Such are the exigencies of sickness in a land without doctors that the memories of the people must be stored with the harvest of centuries.

An ancient Arab historian, in recording the treasures found by the Moslem conquerors at Toledo, mentioned not only the gold, silken stuffs, and precious stones, but gave equal place and importance to the treatises on plants and recipes of simples and elixirs. Treasured then, this knowledge of plants is treasured still in New Mexico—where the doctors, who have come only since the railroad, are accepted as an afterthought, a last resort in extremity.

To the herder of sheep and to the farmer of beans it is enough that the earth is beneficent and that the uses of its plants are known to him and to his wife and chiefly to the *médica,* who is midwife, nurse, doctor, and all. Priest she cannot be, but if death comes to one of her patients, the brotherhood of *Los Hermanos Penitentes* may take charge and a wake will be held in the house. Often the hymns are of a nature more ancient than the sect itself, which had its inception in the Third Order of Saint Francis and which is characterized by its yearly penitential practices of self-inflicted pain, voluntary scourging, and even crucifixion. Long has

12

it served the religious needs of an ardent, lonely people often too isolated or too poor for the frequent attentions of a priest. The local *Hermano Mayor,* or head brother, may lead in a burial service and, as with a *médica,* the cost will be slight.

When coin is scarce, a *médica* will welcome produce for her recompense and always in her storeroom you will see corn and beans, onions and chile crowding the roots and herbs of her own harvest. "It is best", she will say, "to gather your remedies in the Autumn when its full strength has come into the plant". Many of her beliefs are true survivals from medieval Europe and include a respect for the magic of numbers, the tenets of witchcraft, the use of oriental spices, and the Doctrine of Signatures. Hers is the same effort to understand that man has made through the ages, and she will graciously share her knowledge with one like myself, whose only credential is a kindred interest.

Two or three common herbs plucked from the roadside before approaching her house, and a smiling *"Buenas tardes",* are introduction enough for an invitation of *"Entra, entra!"* When we have sat down and spoken of the weather and the tidy whitewashed room, we are soon friends and it is my turn to show knowledge. I indicate a familiar plant in my hand and recite its virtues: "This is *mastranzo,*" I will say, "very good for the cough or for colds in the chest." *"Sí, sí!"* she responds, and her face brightens quickly with enthusiasm. "It is *very* good; and mixed with a little honey it is best." Here, already, is an occasion for my pencil and notebook, since I have not known of the honey ingredient before.

Often when I visit one of these *médicas* in her modest adobe house, her clothes perhaps frayed and worn, I am amazed at her ability and her memory, at her self-reliance and at all the good that she has accomplished among her people. She has brought comfort and relief to suffering, armed only with her simple remedies derived from nature. I look about me and there is no equipment. Her cures are in her mind, in her garden, far in the mountains or out on the plains. Her tools are her wonderful hands, so small, so magnetic and eloquent of healing. She is the Temple of Hope for those in need, as she is the source and essence of this book.

L. S. M. CURTIN

ACEITE MEXICANO

MEXICAN OIL

Patent medicines, if their directions are implicitly followed, leave no play to the imagination; but since the Spanish New Mexicans are both a very imaginative and a resourceful people, they often adapt commercial medicines to their own purposes. In this manner, Mexican Oil, a patent medicine, is taken, one-half teaspoonful at a time, in hot water, with a little sugar, for pains in the intestines. It is also included in recipes, with native remedies, as will be seen elsewhere in this book.

ACEITE DE LA VÍBORA

RATTLESNAKE OIL

Rattlesnake oil largely was collected from the snakes on the Mexican border, and is said to have furnished a livelihood to a large number of "collectors" who sold it at the standard price of a dollar an ounce.

This *aceite* was in demand as a remedy against rheumatism; and since it was supposed to absorb the poison, it was used as a cure for snakebite.

Many and varied were the resorts in case of snakebite, but whiskey, used externally, and especially internally, was the most common. According to an article in the 1929 edition of "Folk-say", on "Animal Fats in Folk Medicine"; "The warm flesh of the freshly-killed snake that bit you would draw out the poison from the wound. The root of the prairie or buffalo gourd, beaten up and put into sweet milk, was an antidote to snake bite. This milk was taken internally and used to bathe the wound also. A tea made of the root of 'nigger head' would cure snakebite".

If a rattlesnake should bite a sheep, the Spanish New Mexicans cut the wound open, wash it with salt and water, and cover the incision with mud.

15

AGUA PIEDRA

Agua piedra, found in caves, is a deposit that supposedly has been formed by the mineral content of water so that long narrow stone-like deposits, resembling a bone on one side and a stone on the other, are produced. A medicine-man of San Juan pueblo, serene of aspect and wrinkled of visage, declared that a small quantity of this substance is powdered and given in hot water to those with kidney trouble or stomach afflictions.

AGUAPÁ

CATTAIL   Typha latifolia L.
CATTAIL FAMILY   Typhaceæ

One seldom fails to see, throughout the United States, in marshy land the familiar brown-topped wands of the cattail rising above a thick mass of long slender leaves. Its roots contain a nutritious secret which evidently was formerly known only to the Indians, who dug and ground them into a meal, but now chemical analysis has revealed that they contain a core of nearly solid starch, equal in food value to rice and corn.

Maya texts, which refer to the cattail as *puh,* say that its leaves were made into rush mats, and rural Mexicans still thatch their roofs with *aguapá* stalks before covering them with a final layer of adobe. At present, Spanish New Mexicans weave its leaves into baskets, and sometimes stuff their pillows with the silky down from the sausage-shaped inflorescence at the tips of the stalks.

M. R. Harrington, in a delightful article, "The Cat-tail Eater", which appeared in the September, 1933, "Masterkey", a publication of The Southwest Museum, relates an experience with an elderly Paiute woman: "The old lady brought from a wickiup a pack-basket full of the 'tails' and carried them to a place prepared for the purpose—a bit of hard ground,

16

carefully cleared and smoothed, five or six feet across. Here she shelled enough down from the stalks to cover an area a yard in diameter to the depth of half an inch or so. Then she did an unexpected thing: she got up and went back into the wickiup, returning a few minutes later with a limber switch and a blazing stick from her campfire.

"Kneeling, she touched the fire to the down and began to agitate it vigorously with the switch. Almost instantly the flame ran through it, consumed it, and died away. But the seeds were not consumed; there they lay . . . 'Taste them', she said in Paiute. I did, and found them good, with, if I remember, a sort of nutty flavor".

AJO

GARLIC   Allium sativum L.
ONION FAMILY   Liliaceæ

One of the old Spanish proverbs, *suspirar por los ajos y cebollas de Egypto*—"to sigh for the garlic and onions of Egypt", i.e., to desire a return to the wicked life that has passed—may have some connection with the fact that garlic formed part of the food of the Isrælites in Egypt, and of the laborers who built the great pyramid of Cheops.

Garlic is described by John Minsheu, who published at London, in 1627, "The Guide into the Tongues": "It is of most especial use among sea-faring men, and a most excellent preservative against all infection proceeding from the nastie savour of the pumpe and stinke in a ship, and of tainted and corrupt meats, which Mariners are faine to eat for fault of better . . . The Spaniard therefore, as it seems, having colder stomacks than other countries, doth well brooke the smell hereof, when everie day before he goeth out of his Inne, as he journieth, he causeth garlicke to be stamped, crums of bread and oile to be fried together in the manner of a hastie pudding, and so eateth thereof; and the commonsort doe live by it, so that it is the poor mans Physicke and Food".

17

And another saying reflects this belief: *ajo puro y vino crudo, passan el puerto segúro,* "pure garlic and wine help one to traverse safely the high mountain passes". In Spain, such passes were called dry spots, and wine and garlic were a good defense for travelers.

The garlic is of old English origin, *gárleác (gar* meaning spear; *leac,* leek or lance) is one of its early forms.

Since its introduction by the Spanish, it has had many different uses in the vicinity of Santa Fé.

When a horse is *malo* (suffering from a swollen neck), garlic is crushed with the twigs of *Sabino macho* (mule pine), and hot water is added. This is allowed to cool and is then administered.

As a preventive against diphtheria, garlic is strung on a string and worn around the neck by people who are in contact with the disease.

An informant in Galisteo told me she knew of a remedy that gave immediate relief for pain in the bowels on the left side. Two garlic buttons are baked soft, then crushed; a little cold water is added, and the mixture drunk.

One crushed button, pressed against the gum, lessens toothache.

When a dog is suspected of having rabies, garlic should be mixed with its food immediately. This also serves as a vermifuge and is a very common ministration in New Mexico.

Besides numerous dishes that are flavored with garlic, it is also believed that it counteracts stomach trouble and flatulency. It is roasted whole on coals, cleaned, thoroughly chewed, and swallowed with cold water. The gas then disappears, and other discomforts are alleviated.

Moreover, garlic is used in one of the many treatments for snakebite. A fresh poultice, made from the mashed plant, should be applied thrice daily. Even as far afield as North Africa, the same remedy is given for hornet and scorpion stings, and garlic is eaten there with honey and rancid butter for the kidneys and bladder.

18

It is not surprising that, in rural New Mexico, charms should play so important a part in the lives of its inhabitants. So when a young girl wishes to rid herself of an undesirable suitor, she must choose a spot where two roads "make a cross" and there, on the ground, she must place two crossed pins and a piece of garlic. When this has been done, the girl must then find some means of making the despised young man walk over the charm, quite unaware of its presence. If she be successful she will be freed from his attentions ever after, so the old people say.

Not long ago, I received the following letter, with its amusing Spanish, from a Santa Clara Indian, testifying to the curative properties of garlic for earache: *"Yo estube alle pregunte las muge del remedio y me dise el ajo y sal puesto lana de norego y a que tomo la pluma en mi mano con el mas grande gusto y placeres para Saludarles a V. V. paro decirle que nosotro estamos buenos"*. Briefly, his note states, "I was over there and asked the woman about a remedy for my ear, and she says garlic and salt placed on lamb's wool and put in the ear. We are all well and hope you are likewise".

ÁLAMO DE HOJA REDONDA

VALLEY COTTONWOOD   Populus wislizeni Wats.
WILLOW FAMILY   Salicaceæ

How grateful the *conquistadores* must have been for the large cottonwoods which gave them shelter on their journeys and guided them to water, later providing shade in their *plazas* and along their *alamedas!*

Americans now prefer to plant only the male of the species, as the female trees litter their surroundings with cotton. On the other hand the Spanish and Mexican settlers, especially the children, prized—and still do—the young green pods of the female cottonwood which provide for them an early relief from their winter diet.

Álamo bark, leaves, and branches all had their uses. The

19

former was burned and the ashes mixed with corn-meal and water to make a poultice for boils. Even black boils yielded to this treatment, turning white and healing rapidly. The leaves of the tree were boiled in water and the decoction taken to relieve dropsy.

Before modern methods of treating bone fractures were known, a large quantity of the rough bark was simmered for an entire day in a big tub of water, care being taken to keep the fire low. The liquid was strained, returned to the fire, and cooked until it reached the consistency of honey. After a broken bone had been set, this thick syrup was spread over the break, or placed on a cloth and wrapped tightly about the fracture. Additional bandaging was considered unnecessary since the syrup hardened enough to serve as both splint and wrapping. Such was the nature of this remarkable cast that it remained in place about two months, only disintegrating when the bone had had ample time to knit. The use of a little oil facilitated its final removal.

Even now, in Truchas, a similar method of treatment survives; the branches, instead of the bark, are boiled to obtain the syrup. When this has hardened over the fracture, a splint of the curved bark is used as reinforcement.

To the Pueblo Indians, the bole of the large cottonwood is of foremost importance, as it is from this tree-trunk that their drums are fashioned. A selected section is hollowed out by burning and scraping to form the resonant frame for their double-headed instrument. From the light thick root, furthermore, the Hopi of Arizona carve their sacred Katchina dolls.

ÁLAMO SAUCO

MOUNTAIN COTTONWOOD　　　　　Populus angustifolia
NARROW-LEAFED COTTONWOOD
WILLOW FAMILY　　　　　　　　　Salicaceæ

This cottonwood, the leaves of which are somewhat similar to those of the graceful willow, also borders mountain streams and offers its shade to men and animals.

A *médica* will advise robbing the ripe fruit, dipping the cotton in water, and placing the pad on a swollen gum, believing it will reduce inflammation. And when some one has an ulcerated tooth, a similar method is employed.

The old world-wide custom of purifying the blood in the springtime was followed by steeping the fresh flowers for several hours in cold water. The resultant infusion was then strained and drunk.

ALBÁCA

ALBÁCAR　　　　　　　　　　　Ocimum Basilicum L.
ALVÁCAR
ALVÁCA
ALBACARÓN
ALBAHACA
SWEET BASIL
MINT FAMILY　　　　　　　　　　Labiatæ

"This is the herb which all authors are together by the ears about, and rail at one another, like lawyers . . . And away to Dr. Reason went I, who told me it was an herb of Mars, and under the Scorpion, and therefore called basilion, and it is no marvel if it carry a kind of virulent quality with it. Being applied to the place bitten by venemous beasts, or stung by a wasp or hornet, it speedily draws the poison to it. Hilarius, a French physician, affirms upon his own knowledge, that an acquaintance of his, by common smelling to it, had a scorpion bred in his brain. It expelleth both birth and after-birth"—Culpeper.

"Take a little green basil, and when men bring the dishes

21

to the table put it underneath them, that the women perceive it not; for men say that she will eate of none of that which is in the dishes whereunder the basil lieth"—Alexis of Piemont.

Thus it was in other lands; in New Mexico sweet basil is believed to have the curious property of bringing luck and money to those who carry it in their pockets.

Furthermore, the leaves are ground, mixed with sweet oil, and dropped into the ear to alleviate earache; and beaten eggs, mixed with the powdered leaves, are applied on chest and back for cold and pneumonia.

The entire plant is boiled and taken as a tea for weak stomach and lack of appetite, and enough of the plant to color water, with the addition of *piloncillo,* is given lukewarm to babies for colic. It is generally considered that a pinch of *albáca,* when eaten and followed by a small glass of water, acts as an emmenagogue.

In order to induce children to take it, a little sugar and nutmeg are added to a decoction of the leaves, to remedy diarrhea, and, at Tularosa, cornstarch is put into a similar preparation for the same thing.

I have been interested to find that sweet basil still is being used in New Mexico, as it was in Culpeper's time, to decrease the trials of childbirth, for a tea is given here during parturition. It has also been asserted that if the green leaves are eaten or drunk as a decoction, they relieve menstrual pains.

Although it was on a safe day when no *brujas* could overhear us, a practitioner in white magic, with eyes afire, whispered in my ear this formula for recalling "straying husbands": "The neglected wife must grind a packet of *alváca* on an ax with another piece of iron so that it won't stick as it would on stone. Then she divides a paper into five bits, puts a pinch of the powder on each, and folds it. In the evening after she has gone to bed, one packet is emptied into her hands, which are rubbed together as she says *'Que Dios me ayude'* (May God help me!). Then her neck, shoulders, breast, armpits,

22

and especially the region over the heart are dusted with the powder. When all the portions have been used, her husband becomes a veritable saint".

ALBARICOQUE, HUESO DE

APRICOT   Prunus Armeniaca L.
ALMOND FAMILY   Drupaceæ

Strange indeed has been the apricot's history, as the memoirs of its names and travels show. It was domesticated in Northern China, and its descendants moved by overland caravans to Armenia and settled. Hence the name Armeniaca. Fray Alonso de Benavides encountered the apricot in New Mexico and included it in his list of the flora he knew there in 1629.

The English word, formerly "apricock", and "abrecox," comes from the French *abricot,* taken from the Spanish *albaricoque,* which was derived from the Arabic *alburquk,* itself a rendering of the Latin adaptation of the Greek.

In contrast to general practice, its medicinal use is limited to the ground kernel of the pit. This is placed within the nostrils of babies suffering from dryness of the nose, and a poultice, similarly prepared, is applied to the throat for goitre.

ALCANFOR

CAMPHOR   Cinnamomum Camphora Nees &
                                               Eberm.
LAUREL FAMILY   Lauraceæ

Who has not put a cake of camphor with his silver, or taken a pungent tablet when a cold began? And who has not wondered whence came this aromatic preserver of tableware and of health? The Yellow sea washed its birthplace, the Indian ocean tempered its adopted home. Many languages combined to bring its name—Sanskrit and Persian, Arabic, Latin, and Spanish—to American shores.

Our Spanish New Mexicans, being of a practical turn,

maintain their formula is better than commercial camphorated oil. They advise putting pork lard and a cake of camphor in a fifteen-cent baking-powder tin, which should be covered and allowed to stand in boiling water until the camphor is melted. This preparation is excellent for all kinds of pains.

Furthermore, camphor mixed with whiskey, is rubbed on rheumatic joints.

The crystalline cakes are often kept in readiness for headaches and faintness, as their aroma relieves these conditions.

ALEGRÍA

RED COCKSCOMB   Amaranthus paniculatus L.
LADY BLEEDING
PRINCESS FEATHER
AMARANTH FAMILY   Amaranthaceæ

W. W. H. Davis, the author of "El Gringo", published in 1857, observed the following while stopping at the Pontius Pilate House at Chamita, New Mexico:

"They (the mother and daughter of the pious Pilate family) had their faces besmeared with the crimson juice of the *alegría* plant, and looked most frightful and disgusting. A thick coating covered the whole face, which gave them the appearance of wearing masks, with the eyes, nose, and mouth uncovered. This was the first exhibition of the kind I had seen, and it struck me as such a filthy and singular custom, that I was not slow to inquire the cause of it. Afterward, I noticed the same in all parts of the Territory, and found it to be a common and cherished practice among the village and country beauties. It is done for the purpose of protecting the skin from the sun, and they will remain in this repulsive condition two or three weeks upon the eve of a grand baile or feast at which they may desire to appear in all their freshness and beauty. The cream of the matter is, that in most instances the complexion of the wearer is about the color of seasoned

24

mahogany, and upon which all the sun from the north to the south pole could make no impression. Besides *alegría* they make use of clay and starch in the same manner, and at times you will see these three colors displayed upon the visages of as many members of the same family. Perchance this belle of Chamita had been doing penance in a smeared face for several days, in order to appear in her most witching charms during the season of the court; and who knows but that ambitious thoughts had crept into her maidenly heart, and that she even hoped to be able to captivate one of the *Gringos* who might quarter at the Pontius Pilate? How do my fair countrywomen like this improvement in a lady's toilet?"

Cockscomb was brought into this region by the Spaniards, and although carefully tended in their little gardens, it gradually escaped from cultivation, and is becoming naturalized in various places.

At Taos, many find it helpful in treating heart trouble. The flowers are boiled and strained, and, to this tea, cinnamon and a very little *piloncillo* (Mexican brown sugar) are added. A small glass is drunk as often as seems necessary.

Some of the inhabitants of La Bajada make a bath with red cockscomb for tuberculosis, heart trouble, and jaundice. In curing jaundice, certain directions are followed implicitly: the flowers are allowed to stand four days in a glass of water, and then the strained infusion is placed on a shaded window-sill. The patient looks at it and the jaundiced eye is supposed to clear as the liquid gradually fades.

Alegría also plays an important part in the toilet of Zuñi maidens, since the leaves and blossoms, crushed and moistened with spittle or water, are rubbed on their cheeks as rouge. Furthermore, they color their *héwe*, ceremonial wafer bread, with the feathery part of the plant.

The Hopi Indians put it to a similar use in the preparation of their ceremonial bread, *píki*, which is baked in thin sheets, and, while still warm, rolled. Several cylinders are then tied together, one on top of another, and the whole string is carried by the Kachinas in various dances for distribution among favored spectators.

The word amaranth, or amarant, is from the Greek, and means unwithering. The name was given to a number of plants that faded very slowly, and therefore were considered symbols of immortality.

ALFALFA

ALFALFA   Medicago sativa L.
LUCERNE
PURPLE MEDIC
PEA FAMILY   Legummosæ

If one tried to enumerate those things which he associated with the Southwest—chile, cactus, chamiso, cattle-guards, cowboys, arroyos, mesas, Indians, drought, sand, heat, mud, and wind, to mention only a few—he would have to include alfalfa in the picture.

Aside from its tremendous value as forage for stock, the Spanish New Mexicans aver that if you place the green cuttings around a room, they make an excellent barrier against *chinches,* bedbugs; that it will scare them all away, for they do not like its smell.

Because of its highly nutritious properties, the latest Government reports have advised alfalfa as "greens" for human consumption.

The Spanish word, *alfalfa,* like so many others in that language beginning with "al", is of Arabic derivation, the term in the latter tongue being *alfaçfaçah.*

ALFALFÓN

SWEET CLOVER   Melilotus alba Desr.
PEA FAMILY   Leguminosæ

It resembles true alfalfa and, when in bloom, attracts the bees with its fragrance. It is not considered, however, nourishing fodder for native livestock.

26

The flowering plant often sweetens linen carefully stored away in chests and closets and is sometimes placed between mattresses as a protection against bedbugs.

If its cut branches are hung up in a room, says native lore, they will attract all the flies, which can be eliminated by throwing out the spray after dark.

ALFILERILLO

ALFILERÍA   Erodium cicutarium L'Her.
RED-STEMMED FILAREE
STORKSBILL
CLOCKS
PINKETS
PINCLOVER
THREAD AND NEEDLE
CRANESBILL FAMILY   Geraniaceæ

Filaree was introduced from Southern Europe, and later served as a particularly valuable forage plant in the Southwest; and like many naturalized weeds, it has spread over most of the United States.

Evidently the long, slender seed vessels, resembling a bird's beak or a pin, have played an important part in the naming of this plant. The Greeks and Romans obviously were influenced thereby, since *Erodium* referred to a heron and *Geranium* to a crane. The common term in New Mexico at present is *alfilerillo,* which is the Spanish diminutive for pin. Looking farther back, we find that the Arabic word, *al filal,* was introduced by the Moors into Spain. Their name for it, however—unlike the Spanish—means "fingers of stork".

When a diuretic is required, a handful of *alfilerillo* is boiled in a pint of water, strained, and the tea is drunk while tepid. A bath is made for rheumatism and other maladies by boiling larger quantities.

A remedy for gonorrhea *(purgación),* is concocted similarly with a handful of filaree, an equal quantity of *yerba del burro* (Distichlis spicata Greene), with a small piece of *pil-*

27

oncillo (Mexican brown sugar) and one or two of the dry leaves that come from México around the cone of *piloncillo*. A glassful, lukewarm, is drunk morning and night until the cure is effected.

ALHUCEMA

LAVENDER
MINT FAMILY

Lavandula Spica L.
Labiatæ

Even D. Rembert Dodoens, the Elizabethan herbalist, in many cases divided plants according to the sexes.

"Lavender is of two sortes", he writes, "male and female. The male hath his leaves, floures, spikie ears, and stemmes, broader, longer, higher, thicker, and of a stronger savour. The female is smaller, shorter, and of a pleasanter savour".

The leaves and flowers of lavender are said to have been used by the ancients to perfume their baths; hence the Mediterranean Latin name *Lavandula* is supposed to have been derived from *lavare,* to wash. Of course the Spanish name is pure Arabic.

This fragrant flower was brought from Spain to the New World, and is carefully guarded within the houses during the winter months.

A sick room often is fumigated by sprinkling the lavender on a brass platter containing red-hot embers, and three days after a child is born, the mother is covered with a sheet and is purified by the plant's incense. Fumigation is used also to facilitatae a difficult childbirth.

For phlegm in small babies, the nursing mother is given a tea made of the boiled seeds, or the seeds are chewed and placed in a small bag and put in the baby's mouth.

When newly-born infants suffer from colic produced by first milk, a tea is made from the dry leaves, a little *piloncillo* is added, and the liquid is applied to the mother's nipple.

A few of the dry leaves are taken to relieve vomiting, and a tea is prepared for stomach trouble.

Alhucema and *manzanilla* (Matricaria courrantina DC.). provide relief for menopause when the flow is excessive; the two herbs are mixed, well ground, placed on a heated cloth, and applied.

During the seventeenth century in England, according to Culpeper, lavender allayed the pangs of colic and other maladies.

At the present time, it is employed in the pharmacopœia as an adjuvant to other medicines.

ALMÁCIGA DE SABINA

(Juniper pitch)

ONE-SEEDED JUNIPER   Juniperus monosperma (Engelm.) Sarg.

CYPRESS FAMILY   Cupressaceæ

Spanish New Mexican children and Indians sometimes chew juniper pitch instead of commercial chewing gum, and parents of the former, to counteract swelling in the face, grind white beans and *marrubio* (horehound) with the resin, and rub it on the afflicted parts.

ALTAMISA DE LA SIERRA

Artemisia franserioides Greene

ASTER FAMILY   Compositæ

It was Sunday, and I was on one of my frequent trips to increase my acquaintance with native herbs. I stopped before a promising adobe house standing alone by its cornfield.

After greeting me with a cheerful *buenas tardes,* "good afternoon," the black-clad elderly woman who appeared in the irregular moulding of her doorway asked me to enter. I accepted with pleasure. And as she removed her protecting

29

tapalo, I was amazed at the nobility and quietude of an expression that it shaded.

"Is that your son?" I ventured to inquire, referring to a heavily framed picture, conspicuously hung on the wall.

"He is my eldest," she replied. "He works in the mountains."

Just then I saw two small bundles of *altamisa de la sierra* tied together with yucca leaves, and suspended from a viga. "And does he bring the *altamisa* down to you?"

"The *altamisa?* Oh, yes!" Her slight embarrassment had vanished with my mention of the herb. A deeper interest took its place. "My grandson has the colic. We give him the fresh leaves to chew with a little salt; there is nothing better."

I saw I had gained her confidence, and after a little prodding, I found that she also made a tea from the dry or ground leaves to relieve bad colds, stomach ache, and diarrhea.

Hardly another plant in the country enjoys so favored a reputation, and exclamations of praise will invariably follow the mention of its name. "I have taken gallons of it", said one man. "My mother always gave it to me as a child, and it is very good".

I later learned at Agua Fría that *altamisa de la sierra* is included in one of the composite remedies which are comparatively rare in New Mexico. For constipation, suppositories are made of the dry leaves of *añil del muerto* (Verbesina encelioides Cav.), *altamisa, punche mexicano* (local tobacco); and bound with honey, *piloncillo* (Mexican brown sugar), and *jabón de trementina* (laundry soap). Then, if needed, a mixture of *azahar* (dry orange blossoms) and lard is steamed and employed in coating the suppositories.

Altamisa mexicana is used for the same ailments in the same way; it is the next entry.

ALTAMISA MEXICANA

FEATHERFEW   Chrysanthemum parthenium Pers.
FEVERFEW
WHITE WORT
ST. PETER'S WORT
ASTER FAMILY   Compositæ

In addition to the remedies I have already described, this *altamisa*, when boiled in large quantities, also acts as a menostatic in a sitz bath.

Furthermore, it is interesting to find that feverfew, during the seventeenth century in England, was given for most of the same maladies.

AMOLILLO

WILD LICORICE   Glycyrrhiza lepidota Nutt.
PEA FAMILY   Leguminosæ

Amolillo is a perennial, herbaceous plant with tall erect slender stems, at time reaching ten feet in height, and has odd-pinnate leaves and racemes of inconspicuous greenish-white flowers. It is closely related to the Old World licorice, which furnishes a living to large numbers of northern Syrians who gather the roots upon inland downs and carry them to Alexandretta for shipment.

The word licorice is descended through the French and Latin from the ancient Greek, *glykys,* sweet, and *rhiza,* root.

The local folkname was given to the plant because the early settlers soon noticed that its roots would foam like those of *amole* when stirred in water. Hence the name *amolillo* with its suffix implying similarity, in the same way we make rosette from rose.

One summer, while scrambling over the ruins of a distant Indian pueblo, I came upon some faint wagon-tracks so appealing in their direction that we simply had to follow them. My car soon became a combined kangaroo and porpoise that would have put the celebrated jumping frog of Calaveras

31

County to shame. Such was the "road"—where could it lead among these dry foothills spotted with stunted junipers? A willow-sheltered streamlet at last sweetened the way and soon there was a house; farther along there was another, and the place was called Ciruela. A woman surrounded by ten children appeared in one of the doorways and with a cheerful smile asked me to enter. My car was the first she had seen in a year. The conversation turned to the use of *amolillo* and the kindly *señora* told me that her children had been born while she was alone and unattended. She had found that *amolillo* roots washed, mashed and frothed in water, strained through a cloth and a glass taken three times a day before meals, beginning the third day after parturition and continuing until the flow came, had greatly helped her. She especially recommended this remedy in cases of retention of the afterbirth, or when fever developed in the mother.

Not long after, another mother informed me that a handful of the roots, crushed and stirred in a quart of water, but not strained, and drunk instead of plain water, made a good cleanser of the uterus.

At Prado, for clotted blood, caused by an accident, or for a wound caused by a shot, the ground root is beaten up in water, and the water and foam are drunk until the clotted blood is carried off.

In Chimayo, raw rice is ground fine, a tablespoonful added to a glass of strained *amolillo* tea, and drunk three times a day before meals as an emmenagogue.

AMORES

WILD COSMOS   Cosmos parviflorus (Jacq.) H.B.K.
ASTER FAMILY   Compositæ

Naturally, wild cosmos is much smaller than the garden variety, though they greatly resemble one another. *Amores* (lovers), is the name given to the former because of the "affectionate" tendency of its seeds to embrace the passer-by.

32

I often find that a plant is used for different remedies in separate localities, and this is true of the wild cosmos. In Prado, north of Taos, the tea is suggested as a purge. Elsewhere, a similar brew is offered for children suffering from cold in the chest; and at La Bajada, where the cultivated cosmos is called "tostón", its dried flowers, taken as a tea, are supposed to relieve whooping cough. It is amusing to speculate on the origin and formation of this local Spanish name. Can it be that the good people of La Bajada have found the combination of *tos*, cough, and the augmentative *ton*, the proper word for the plant as they drank its tea in the paroxysms of whooping-cough?

AÑIL

CASTILL (La Bajada, N. M.)   Helianthus annuus L.
MIRASOL (Spanish)
GIRASOL (Spanish)
SUNFLOWER
ASTER FAMILY   Compositæ

The genus Helianthus, from the Greek *helios*, sun, *anthos*, flower, contains about fifty species, chiefly natives of North America, a few being found in Perú and Chile. In New Mexico, during the early autumn, when many other flowers have passed, its brilliant yellow petals, surrounding a rich brown center, embellish many roadsides with a golden fringe.

"This plante groweth in the Weste India, the which is called America. Of the virtue of this herbe and floure, we are able to say nothing, because the same hath not bene yet found out, or proved of any man"—Dodœns.

Sagard-Theodat, a French Franciscan missionary—who published, in 1636, a "History of Canada"—was astonished at finding the Indians cultivating and using the sunflower "The girls reduce the seed to flour", he writes, "in the big mortar, then put it to boil in a large kettle of water, and after a while the oil swims on top of the soup, which the

33

savages gather with their horn spoons into their gourd bowls; and not only is this oil good to eat, but also the pounded seed, which the savages esteem an excellent thing, and which I have tasted with approval".

Lewis and Clark record in the reports on their famous northwestern exploration that they found the Indians of those regions using it, and that they themselves occasionally enjoyed a dish of sunflower-seed meal mixed with marrow grease.

Truly, its wide adaptability to various needs reminds one of the Brazilian tree of life. The flower furnishes a yellow dye, and honey; the seeds, oil, food, and a dull gray-blue dye; its leaves are good for fodder, and its hardy stalk contains a textile fiber. At present, sunflowers are widely cultivated, being grown in increasing quantities in California as well as Russia, Egypt, and India. It is said that the yellow sweet oil from the seeds equals olive oil for the table, and sunflower oil-cake is exported by Russia to Denmark and Sweden for stock feeding.

The Zuñi employ the plant to cure rattlesnake bite, and among the Tewa Indians the fire-stick for lighting cigarettes sometimes is a dried sunflower stalk. Although treatments for respiratory afflictions often were the same—the various types of bronchitis, lung infections, and pleurisy not being distinguished—a decoction of the sunflower head was administered by the Dakota and Pawnee Indians for such maladies.

Indians also made a yellow dye by boiling the petals, and this coloration is used in basketry by the Hopi of Arizona. Erna Fergusson, in her book, "Dancing Gods", alludes to the use of sunflowers in the Lalakonti ceremonial by the Hopi Indians. "All eyes turned to the *kiva*", she writes, "and then we saw Lakone and the two Lakonemana. Lakonetaka was a yellow and white figure; his face, body, and arms and legs were painted yellow with the sunflower pollen, and he wore white ceremonial garments . . . They told us that yellow was the color of the North".

34

In the small village of La Bajada, where this annual herb is called *castillo,* I was told that a bath is prepared with the green or dry leaves for rheumatism and pains in the bones.

Añil, with the accent on the first syllable, is the local name for sunflower, but *añil,* with the accent upon the last syllable, is the local word for bluing. The Spanish dons brought indigo (which they called *añil*) and sheep with them from old Méxi-co, and taught the Indians how to weave and color their wool-en blankets. Hence the local word for the present-day com-mercial bluing probably is a result of this introduction.

The Indians used to test the indigo by dipping a piece in water and lighting it, the flame determining whether or not it was of the desired quality.

Bluing is now given to horses for heaves. And for indi-gestion, one drop of quicksilver bought at a pharmacy, and three or four of bluing in one-half cup of water is administered. Bluing also is advised in this vicinity, taken internally with luke-warm water, as a vermifuge for people, horses, and dogs.

AÑIL DEL MUERTO

GOLD WEED
CROWNBEARD
ASTER FAMILY

Verbesina encelioides Cav.

Compositæ

The soft gray foliage and profuse yellow flowers of *añil del muerto* add a colorful fringe to tawny roadsides and fallow fields throughout a long season. It is a convenient and com-mon plant, quickly found and easily gathered. No wonder it has many uses.

For stomach trouble the leaves are pulverized, and taken with a little cold water; or a tea is made from the plant. A similar preparation is administered for rheumatism and as a menostatic, or, with the addition of cinnamon, cloves, and a little soda, it may be imbibed while hot, for diarrhea. The crushed plant with salt is good for swellings.

In the treatment of cancer or sores, the plant, including

35

the flower head, is ground fine and put through a sieve. Oil is applied to such disorders which are then sprinkled with the powder.

A radical remedy for piles is an equal mixture of powdered *añil del muerto* and *punche* (a local tobacco), which is placed on a warm cloth and applied to the affliction.

The dry leaves are ground, mixed with dry *cal* (lime), and rubbed on the limbs for dropsy.

The mysterious malady called "swelling of the lungs" is treated three times a day for nine days with a draught of one teaspoonful of dry ground leaves, one of sugar, and a drop of vinegar in a glass of cold water. The same beverage is taken for liver trouble. Here again the influence of the magic of numbers is striking.

ANÍS

ANISE   Pimpinella anisum L.
PARSLEY FAMILY   Umbelliferæ

Anís, long famous for its savory qualities and gentle aroma, was even included in the medical library of that powerful eighth century (B. C.) Assyrian king, Assurbanipal, and in the four hundred "simples" of Hippocrates.

The cavaliers of sixteenth century England believed that "the seede therof bounde in a little bagge or handecarcheff and kept to the nose to smell unto, keepth men from dreaming, and starting in their sleepe, and causeth them to rest quietly."

It is held in New Mexico that the seeds, ground, toasted and mixed with whiskey and rubbed on painful shoulders and chests, will make the discomfort vanish immediately.

Some of those who have suffered from stomach trouble or from coughs have found relief in *anís* tea, and the same treatment is occasionally given New Mexican babies for colic.

Aside from the use of *anís* in many cooking recipes which rely on it for their success, its ground seeds may be mixed with the grated room of *inmortal,* strained, and drunk with

36

hot water for pneumonia. And a similar preparation of the seeds, with *azahar* (orange blossoms obtained from a pharmacy) and *remolino,* will act as a carminative.

One of the most unexpected suggestions, arising from the discussion of the uses of this plant, was offered by a mother who said that if you have a child who fails to talk when the proper time comes, you must give him *anís* seeds to smoke.

ANISOTE

SAGEBRUSH　　　　　　　　　　Artemisia redolens A. Gray
WORMWOOD
ASTER FAMILY　　　　　　　　　Compositæ

The large genus of Artemisia was named for the wife of Mausolus, who erected in 353 B. C. the Mausoleum, one of the "seven wonders".

At Vallecitos de Los Indios, in the Jémez mountains, a leaf is chewed with salt and washed down with a drink of water, or the whole *anisote* plant is boiled in water, strained, and the tea taken hot for colic and other stomach troubles.

AZAFRÁN

BASTARD SAFFRON　　　　　　　Carthamus tinctorius L.
FALSE SAFFRON
SAFFRON
SAFFLOWER
AMERICAN SAFFRON
ASTER FAMILY　　　　　　　　　Compositæ

Before reaching New Mexico, saffron was cultivated for centuries over a wide area of the earth; the ancient Egyptians included it among their medicines; it is repeatedly mentioned by Homer and other Greek writers, and it is said to have been brought into China during the Mongol invasion. Among the remedies for which saffron was employed were hair wash and skin balm. Culpeper says that it is a very strong cathartic.

In New Mexico, where safflower was introduced by the

Spaniards as a substitute for true saffron, those suffering from measles are treated with it. The dry flowers are soaked in cold water until the latter is stained yellow, the fluid is then strained and taken, half a glass at a time, to bring out the rash and reduce fever.

It also furnishes a yellow dye, and the Hopi Indians use it to color their ceremonial *piki* bread.

The word saffron is derived from the Persian and Arabic, *za'afarán,* and in Morocco we find that the plant is still applied to a number of maladies, the treatments often being reminiscent of those of ancient times. There, a paste made of water, flour, and saffron, spread on boils, is said to open them. It is believed that an ointment made of saffron and butter is efficient in drawing pus from wounds, and healing them. A dram of the crushed seeds of yellow gilly-flower mixed with a dram of saffron may hasten parturition. And the petals, boiled with a shank of mutton, and the stew eaten, supposedly to invigorate the heart. This is also a reminder that it is widely and freely used in flavoring dishes. The safflower seeds, of themselves, provide an oil particularly suitable as a dryer in paint.

BARBASCO

CROTON WEED   Croton texensis (Kl.) Muell. Arg.
SPURGE FAMILY   Euphorbiaceæ

Barbasco is a silvery gray plant, with small whitish flowers, which grows from one to two feet high, depending on the locality. It is found on plains and hills and is common throughout the state; in fact, many roads are so thickly bordered with the weed that its pungent odor is often mistaken for that of a skunk.

In cases of paralysis, the patient is bathed in a strong infusion of croton weed, but a more elaborate, therefore a highly-respected method, is that by which the body first is anointed with honey, then liberally sprinkled with a powder of the dried plant. If this is allowed to remain overnight, its soothing effect will be fully realized. Both kinds of treatment, however, are claimed to be efficacious and even the powder alone, when well rubbed over the skin, will give results.

Certain types of earache may possibly be alleviated by one of the seeds if it is placed in the ear with a bit of cotton or lamb's wool.

To relieve neuralgia or headache, the ground, dry plant or the green leaves are applied to the head; also the smoke of the dried weed may be inhaled for the same complaints.

The powder is kept on hand as a useful purge. As much as will go on the end of a knife may be taken in a quarter of a glass of warm water.

Barbasco, however, gains its greatest favor as a household insecticide. It is thrown on a pan of hot coals in a sealed room whenever it becomes necessary to fumigate against bedbugs, which are a very common pest in the region. Another popular measure is that of putting the plant under the matresses, or it may often be seen hanging in bunches from the rafters.

One day when I was interviewing a jolly old *médica* about this weed, she said in much seriousness, "You take a small grain, place it in your mouth—so, drink a swallow of water and bang, all the bedbugs leave you!"

Croton is called "coyote leaf" by the Zuñi Indians and, like the Spanish Americans, they use it as a purge. Furthermore, they believe in it as a diuretic and as a remedy for the stomach.

On the Hopi mesas where vermin are particularly prevalent, the people mix *barbasco* powder with white-wash for the interior of their houses.

BELLOTA DE SABINA

JUNIPER MISTLETOE   Phoradendron juniperinum Engelm.
MISTLETOE FAMILY   Loranthaceæ

Children of New Mexico enjoy eating juniper mistletoe berries, and swarm over the juniper trees in search of the white or pinkish-white fruit when it is ripe.

The Tewa Indians grind this mistletoe, mix it with hot water, and drink it when they feel a "chill in the stomach". But the Zuñi find it helpful, when mixed with juniper bark, as a tea in promoting muscular relaxation previous to child-birth, and after parturition, to hasten the cessation of cat-aminia.

There is a suggestion of superstition locally attached to the *bellota de sabina*. *"Te dió bellota"* is what people say when some one shows a particular fondness for a certain person. By this, it is implied that mistletoe has been used to bring upon himself, or herself, the devotion of the other.

With a confusing lack of discrimination, juniper berries are also called *bellota de sabina*. A tea made from them is often taken for stomach trouble and purification of the blood.

The same preparation is drunk in cases of *"infermidades ocultas"*, which probably refers to venereal diseases.

BERRO

WATER CRESS   Radicula nasturtium (L.) Britten &
                              Rendle
MUSTARD FAMILY   Cruciferæ

The origin of the word cress is lost in a conflict of Latin and Teutonic roots, but the presence of similar designations in many languages at least evidences wide usage and cultivation. One encounters in literature the common cress (Lepidium sativum) more frequently than the other plants which pass under the vernacular name "cress" but all have antiscorbutic and diaphoretic qualities, and a pungent, mustard-like taste. If seeds of the common cress are spread thickly on flannel, and kept saturated with warm vapor, as from a boiler or tank of boiling water, they will yield a crop within forty-eight hours. In this way they have proven invaluable as an antiscorbutic during arctic voyages.

Although water cress possesses similar properties, the Spanish New Mexicans eat our native plant for the kidneys and for heart trouble, and crush it finely in cold water before taking it to counteract tuberculosis.

BRAZÍL

CHIPPED WOOD   Hæmatoxylon Campechianum L.
LOGWOOD
PEA FAMILY   Leguminosæ

Logwood, so-called because it was imported in logs from Central America, furnished a strong astringent extract, and the chemical hæmotoxylin which produces a brown and brownish-red dye. The Spaniards first brought it into New Mexico to color their blankets and rugs.

But what originally was a dye became a medicine and is used in the treatment of smallpox. One-half cup of the chips is soaked in a large pitcher of cold water until the liquid is very red. The afflicted person drinks it whenever he is thirsty, to make the smallpox break out. Another remedy for this disease is to take one-half pound of salt, well-heated, and mix with a half pound of bran. This is placed in a bag and pressed on the pustules twice a day until they dry up.

Brazíl is also used in the preparation of a remedy for any kind of heart trouble. A teaspoonful of logwood, *Flor de azahar* (orange blossoms), *anis* (anise), and *alegría* (red cockscomb), are boiled in a quart of water. This is strained and *sangre de venado* (dragon's blood) and a teaspoon of *coral preparado* (which was formerly made from coral but is now a red chalk mixture) are added. Most of these ingredients are obtained at the drug store. A small glass of this preparation is taken before meals.

A glassful of water colored bright red with *brazíl* is placed in the window to counteract *fiebre amarilla* (jaundice). The afflicted person must look at it constantly, and the liquid must be changed every day because it turns white rapidly.

For tuberculosis, a hot sponge bath is prepared with logwood boiled in water, and is administered at 11:00 P. M. daily for three days, and some of the decoction is drunk while bathing.

CADILLOS

COCKLEBUR   Xanthium commune Britton
ASTER FAMILY   Compositæ

This common and troublesome weed, which thrives with maddening independence in the same fields where one attempts to overcome the difficulties of growing more useful plants, has adequately provided for the continuance of its species. It produces seed burrs that cling fast to whatever touches them, and which are thus carried away to take root in some other fertile spot.

Not only does it draw a great deal of nourishment from cultivated ground, but in the seedling stage it may also cause the death of young lambs and pigs who are attracted by its inviting green foliage. Moreover, the burrs often become firmly lodged in sheeps' wool, thus detracting from its value, and necessitating their removal from the fibers.

However, *cadillos* has some good points. An oil can be extracted from the burrs and used in paint and varnish. Three *cadillos,* boiled in a cup of water, arrest the worst case of diarrhea. Nor is its utility limited to the burrs, for a poultice made of the leaves and applied to the wound is reputedly a specific for rattlesnake bite. It is obviously impossible to determine the exact origin of the use of *cadillos* for snakebite, but we do know that this is an extremely old remedy, as "The Historie of Plantes", by Dodœns, published in 1578, tells us that "the iuyce of the great Burre, dronken with olde wine, healeth the bitings and stingings of venemous beasts and serpentes".

According to a Santo Domingo Indian, cuts and wounds on stock can be cured easily by mashing the green leaves and burrs, or grinding the dried burrs, then putting them—mixed with lard or salt—on the affected part.

CAL

LIME

Lime often is included with other substances in composite remedies, but it apparently has healing properties of its own as hydrated lime, sprinkled on a cut that has been washed, will stop bleeding. Lime water is mixed with chile in New Mexico, to prevent the ever-present possibility of stomach trouble. It is a frequent ingredient of any dish which employs the native blue cornmeal mush, as it will improve the color. Lime also is in constant use for the preparation of corn as food, and particularly in the making of *posole* (hominy).

There is an interesting fusion of the old with the new in their lime remedy for burns. Sufficient *cal* is placed in water to form a saturated solution. This is mixed with lubricating oil and well-shaken in a bottle. The blisters are pierced and the mixture is applied with a turkey feather.

The people of New Mexico never bought lime: they gathered the gypsum from neighboring quarries themselves. One of the most famous of these is situated just below La Bajada, the declivity passed in going between Santa Fé and Albuquerque.

All adobe buildings in the state were plastered with the white *yeso* (gypsum or calcium sulphate), on the inside and under the *portal*, and the majority still are today. When a new house is being completed or an old one is to be freshened up, the men of the *lugarcito* (hamlet) must first make a journey to the gypsum quarry and load their wagon with chunks of the rock, or they may be saved the long trip by the foresight of some neighbor with an eye for business who already has stocked up on it. The rock is then piled in an oven and burned or baked until it grows soft—a process which may take from half a day to two days. After this, it is pounded into fragments with a hammer or ground on a *metate* and thrown into a copper cauldron—or, in recent times, a galvanized iron tub. A violent stirring begins as hot water is added until a proper consistency for plastering has been attained. About a gallon of paste made of wheat flour and water boiled together, called *poliadas,* is next mixed with the *yeso.* Without *poliadas,* the *yeso* plaster would rub off more readily on one's clothes—most annoying for a young man in his best suit calling on his *señorita,* or for the old lady in her black shawl, setting out for high mass.

Plastering is entirely the woman's province and each female member of the family is an artist in this line. No trowels are used, but, instead, some very important bits of sheepskin. The wool is left on and sheared a little if too long. If a new room is to be plastered, two coats of *yeso* are given the walls and a special skin is kept for the first coast which is not to be employed for the second. When the rough beams and wattles of the ceiling are to be whitened, there is another special piece of sheepskin. This one is smaller than the others so that it may reach the racks and crannies and make matters uncomfortable for the sheltered insects.

When the room is all whitely plastered and a neat baseboard line has been drawn of *tierra negra* (black earth), or *tierra amarilla* (yellow earth), the precious sheepskins are carefully washed and dried and packed away for the next spring cleaning, which may not take place for several years.

CALABAZA MEXICANA

CALABACITA
GARDEN PUMPKIN
GOURD FAMILY   Cucurbitaceæ

Spanish New Mexicans of Prado eat the seeds three times a day as an emmenagogue. Also, they have long been considered an excellent remedy for tapeworm. The inside of the pumpkin seed is ground and one teaspoonful of the powder is mixed in half a glass of water and allowed to stand overnight. It is then taken before breakfast and is supposed to effect its cure within three hours. My informant tells me that she has known of a case when three yards of worms and all the little ones were expelled after the first dose.

The *calabaza de pastel* is so called because it is used to make a highly-prized sweetmeat. The following is a very old recipe: The ripe pumpkin is peeled and the inside meat cut into squares and boiled in alum water. The following day the pulp is boiled for fifteen minutes or until tender in a syrup of sugar and water. This is left standing overnight. The third day it is boiled five minutes and removed from the liquid. It is sprinkled with sugar and allowed to dry in the sun.

CALABAZILLA

CHILICOTE   Cucurbita fœtidissima H.B.K.
CHILICOYOTE
CHILICAYOTE
CUCURBITÁC
CHILI-COJOTE
CHILICOTHE
WILD GOURD
WILD SQUASH
MISSOURI GOURD
MOCK ORANGE
GOURD FAMILY   Cucurbitaceæ

The rank, garlicky odor of its crushed leaves probably suggested the appropriate Latin name given this plant. It is a coarse but decorative creeping vine, adorned with solitary yellow flowers that mimic the pumpkin's, and triangular, bluish-gray, velvety leaves that stand up in hot weather like so many trowels. It is able to survive in quite arid regions where shallow-rooted plants perish; its own roots often measure six feet. In the autumn, the gourds it produces are laid bare by the withered leaves, and resemble spilled oranges—which perhaps accounts for the popular name of "mock orange" given it in California.

Cucurbita is the Latin for gourd, but several of the Spanish names which are applied to the plant in México and the United States Southwest appear to be adaptations of the Aztec, or Nahua, *chichicayotli*.

Some portions of *calabazilla* make a very strong purge; in fact, an overdose can be fatal. The gourd may be cleaned out, filled with water and drunk from after a short time. The resultant liquid is very bitter but most effective. The Tewa Indians grind the roots, stir them in cold water and drink the mixture as a laxative.

Chilicote also contains enough saponin to make it useful as a soap substitute. The fruit pulp is employed in cleaning and washing the hair, and to promote its growth an oil is extracted from the roasted seeds and applied to the scalp. Moreover, clothing is washed and bleached with it, but great care must be taken to rinse the garments well, or irritation of the skin may result when they are worn.

Many New Mexican housewives rub the cut surface of a gourd over a grease spot to remove it from wooden floors.

Two remedies for rheumatism are made from this plant. One is to bake the fruit in an oven, split it open, and rub it, while still hot, on the afflicted parts. And the other is to mix the ground roots with olive oil, *aceite de comer,* and apply. If a horse suffers from saddle sores, a decoction of the roots is supposed to give relief, and a small quantity in a bottle of water is a good cathartic.

A Santo Domingo Indian told me that he was never troubled with bedbugs, as the ground roots mixed with water

46

and sprinkled all over the room banished them immediately. He also said that there is no reason to have a locoed horse or mule. "I can cure him easily by merely giving a mixture of two tablespoons of powdered *calabazilla* root, a few oats, a little bran, and a teaspoon of sulphur".

The early New Mexican women used the gourds as darning balls. And their children play a well-known game with the wild squash seeds. One holds a few of them in his closed fist and another tries to guess their number. The command, *Adivina, buen adivinador!* "guess, good guesser!" often is varied by the question, *Pares o nones?* "odd or even?"

I have been told that the Navajos come to Peña Blanca from the great Santo Domingo fiesta of August 4, to collect the fruit and carry them home to make rattles.

CAÑA AGRIA
CANAIGRE
CANAIGRA

WILD PIEPLANT   Rumex hymenosepalus Torr.
BUCKWHEAT FAMILY   Polygonaceæ

Cañaigre is particularly conspicuous during the latter part of the winter and early spring, because it retains its green foliage after surrounding plants have lost theirs.

The tubers resemble those of a sweet potato or dahlia, and contain a high percentage of tannin. Consequently, they have been used in the preparation of hides, but their slow growth practically prohibits any wide commercial extraction of the chemical.

Everyone has enjoyed Willa Cather's "Death Comes For the Archbishop", and will probably remember the character of the adopted Indian boy. I have known the real Miguel very well for many years and have always admired his perseverence in earning a livelihood for himself and his family by gathering medicinal roots. Every autumn he takes a pack-train high up into the Sangre de Cristo range to the head-waters of the Pecos river, where he camps for weeks. After drying his harvest at home, it is sold to the people and pharmacies of Santa Fé.

During one of my visits with Miguel, I noticed some curious old wooden tools, highly polished by long usage. Never having seen anything like them before, I offered him an opportunity to explain them. He said they were his old tanning tools, and went on to tell me that the hides were soaked for half an hour in lime and water and then shaken to free them from hair. A bucketful of *caña agria* roots was added to one-half a barrel of luke-warm water, and the skins were left there for a half a month. The barrel was tightly covered. At the expiration of the required time, the leather was removed, well-stretched, and "pegged-out" to dry for fifteen days. After that it was ready for the final softening and use. Sometimes *pino real colorado* (literally, royal red pine) was substituted for *caña agria*.

Another method, he continued, was to soak deer and goat pelts for three days in water. A skin is removed and the head is hung on the top of a log which stands upright, and a knife which has been inserted in a curved stick is used to scrape off the hair. The hide is placed in a little water to which boiled brains have been added. These are worked into the hide until the mixture has been absorbed. The skin is suspended overnight to dry and soaked in water the following morning until soft. Then, it is wrung out with a stick until the hide turns black, and the leather is manipulated for half a day, making it soft and ready for use.

In olden times, cow and horse hides, but no burro skins, were made into sole leather, and two-year-old calves' hides into the uppers on lace boots and low shoes with buckles. The shoemakers used wooden lasts and the shoes were pegged with wood. Local tailors fashioned their coats and trousers from deer skin, goat leather, and the hides of castrated kids. Whenever fastenings were necessary, wooden buttons served this purpose.

The *cañaigre* roots also furnish the basis of several local remedies. Perhaps the resourceful person who conceived that well-known advertising slogan, "four out of every five have it", never heard that ground wild pieplant is used as a rinse for pyorrhea. *Cañaigre* tea often is employed as a gargle for sore throats and the powder is applied under the arms or between the legs to reduce skin irritations.

CAÑUTILLO DEL CAMPO

POPOTILLO
TEPOPOTE
CAÑATILLA
MORMON TEA
TEAMSTER'S TEA
BRIGHAM YOUNG WEED
DESERT TEA
SQUAW TEA
JOINT FIR FAMILY

Ephedra torreyana S. Wats.

Ephedraceæ

Broad, thin leaves permit a greal deal of evaporation of moisture, and since desert plants cannot permit such an extravagance, many of them have very small leaves or none at all. In this latter class we find ephedra, a shrubby plant so well adapted to its dry environment that it often dominates large areas. It occurs in several species, but it may always be recognized by its numerous and many-jointed tubular twigs and its brownish to yellow-green color.

There is a suspicion, held by certain botanists in the United States, that our Southwestern knowledge of ephedra's peculiar properties may be due to Mexican trade contact with the Chinese before the United States were formed. It is a definite matter of record that the Chinese doctors have employed an Asiatic species of ephedra for more than twenty centuries. They call their variety *ma-huang,* and prescribe it for headaches, colds, fevers, and skin eruptions. Members of our

49

medical profession have been interested in trying to find some American ephedrine comparable with that of China. But, as yet, none of the shrubs in California, Nevada, or Arizona has yielded satisfactorily the alkaloid which is the active principle. *Anglos* of the Southwest have taken quantities of *cañutillo* tea in the hope of dissipating rheumatic and arthritic pains.

The native species, however, are liberally provided with tannin, and the number of vernacular names which have been given this plant are proof of the reliance desert people, both Red and White, have placed upon its remedial properties. It was adopted by White explorers and frontiersmen as a medicinal drink supposed to act as a blood purifier, and during the early days in California it was regarded highly as a remedy for renal and vesicle disorders. Among these people, also, it was not uncommon as an equivalent, at meals, to tea or coffee; and the Navajos value it as a beverage when they have first prepared the stems by roasting them in their camp fires. The Mescalero Indians take a decoction of the entire plant as an antiblenorrhagic, and the Pimas drank a decoction of its stems as an antiluetic.

Mary Austin states that because of its activating properties on the mucus membrane, the desert tribes of California, on making long journeys with insufficient water, will chew the stems, and they prescribe a tea made of it as a precaution against thirst.

In New Mexico, as in several other states, it has been used in counteracting the so-called "French disease". Here, a big handful of the plant boiled in a quart of water, strained through a cloth, and a glass of the hot liquid taken three times a day an hour before meals is supposed to clear the system of any venereal disease. When the suffering has been alleviated, one must eat a chopped red onion thrice daily, before meals, for six or eight days.

A decoction of the plant is drunk several times a day to reduce fever and to relieve pain in the kidneys. As a diuretic

50

it is boiled in water, and allowed to cool out-of-doors over-night. Then a glass is taken every morning as long as necessary.

CAÑUTILLO DEL LLANO

SCOURING RUSH   Equisetum hiemale L.
HORSETAIL FAMILY   Equisetaceæ

This species is a common mountain reed-like herb occurring along streams and in swampy places. My specimen came from Cañada de los Alamos at an altitude of 7600 feet.

Its common name, scouring rush, probably arose from its silica-filled epidermal cells, rendering it useful as a substitute for the more modern dishmop, during pioneer days in the Southwest. *Cañutillo* means little tube or pipe in Spanish, and, since the plant is hollowed and jointed, children often make whistles from its segments. The older people of the region, suffering from *purgación* (gonorrhea), claim to have found relief in the scouring rush as a remedy.

CAPULÍN

CHOKE CHERRY   Prunus melanocarpa (A. Nels.) Rydb.
RUM CHERRY
ALMOND FAMILY   Drupaceæ

The racemes of white flowers, which are borne on the ends of its mahogany-colored branches, produce, in August and September, black cherries from which a purplish-red dye is extracted. The fruit is gathered for jam, jelly, and marmalade. Wine is made with the fruit juice, sugar, yeast, and water. This is allowed to stand for fifteen days, and is then strained and bottled with the addition of a little more sugar to each bottle. It should be kept for a month before drinking and is considered a good purifier of the blood.

The people of Peña Blanca dig the roots in September (no other month will do) and boil them in water, with a little

51

piloncillo. A small glass of the warm tea is drunk the first thing in the morning and before every meal to relieve inflammation of the stomach. And for rheumatism, a red tea is made from the boiled roots. A small glass of this is drunk and the rest used as a bath.

In the early spring this plant is considered harmful to animals who eat its young leaves, but at this season of the year, if the outer bark is peeled off, its inner layer yields a green dye.

CARDO SANTO

THISTLE   Cirsium undulatum Nutt.
ASTER FAMILY   Compositæ

The thistle renders many more services than might be imagined from its hostile appearance, and its recognition for medicinal purposes dates from antiquity. The Romans called it *carduus,* from which the Spaniards derived *cardo.*

For earache, Spanish New Mexicans mash the roots, warm the resultant juice, and put a few drops of it into the ear with cotton. For pains in the molars, the same part is boiled and the hot tea is held in the mouth. Those who suffer from diarrhea are given a decoction of its roots, and a similar preparation of its flowers is administered three times a day to those seeking relief from gonorrhea. A tea made from the boiled roots is said to hasten parturition.

Suelda consuelda, which has also been identified as a Cirsium, and which is said by the natives never to flower, is highly regarded as a healing application for fractured bones. One method is to mash the leaves and bind them over the broken part; another consists in peeling the root, and chopping it very fine. Still another prescription is to make a poultice from dough, with the crushed roots or green leaves, and two pinches of salt; this should be bound over the break. If the leaves are mashed, the pulp may be applied to relieve stiff neck and muscles taut from nervous strain.

52

While in Morocco, I found that among those few village men who are illiterate, the thistle is used as follows: three stalks are stripped of leaves and are stood so that they support each other over a brazier of hot coals. Some incense is sprinkled on the brazier and a paper on which some mysterious words have been written is placed over the stalks. The heat causes it to fly away. Under the spot where it lands, there is to be found treasure.

CARDO SANTO

THISTLE POPPY   Argemone hispida Gray
POPPY FAMILY   Papaveraceæ

At Cuyamungué, the entire plant is boiled in the preparation of baths for rheumatism, dropsy, and swellings, or the dried roots may be powdered and applied to the afflicted parts for the same ailments.

CEBADILLA
CEBADILLA DE LA SIERRA

DEER'S EARS   Frasera speciosa Dougl.
GENTIAN FAMILY   Gentianaceæ

The *cebadilla* grows high up in the mountains, and its local name, deer's ears, is a translation of the one given it by the Navajos.

It is regarded as an excellent febrifuge in New Mexico. The dry root is ground and mixed with hot water and rubbed on the body with a piece of cotton. Then the patient must be rolled in several blankets, and made to sweat profusely, thus drawing out the fever.

Although it has been known to prove fatal if taken in large quantities, a small dose of the powdered root stirred into one-half glass of lukewarm water is a very effective purge. Some say that a simpler method is to stir a *cebadilla* stem in a glass of milk for the same remedy. The pulverized roots are roasted and rubbed on the afflicted parts for paralysis, and on the forehead, with *inmortal* similarly prepared, for headache.

The ground root is snuffed up the nose at night before retiring, for a bad cold, headache or neuralgia.

I have been told by the Spanish-Americans that its granulated roots make a good insecticide, and are especially useful in exterminating lice. The powder is mixed with a little lard, and applied freely to the head. This is left on for twelve hours; then the hair is shampooed. After such treatment, "not one insect will remain."

CEBOLLA

GARDEN ONION   Allium Cepa L.
LILY FAMILY   Liliaceæ

The familiar onion of the garden is considered an excellent remedy in New Mexico for chillblains when roasted and applied hot, in small sections, twice daily, to the afflicted parts.

And in this vicinity teething babies are made to masticate its stems and leaves so that the pain and swelling in their gums will be reduced.

Walter R. Smith in his article, "Animals and Plants in Oklahoma Folk Cures", published in "Folk-say—A Regional Miscellany", 1929, Oklahoma Folk-Lore Society, shows that onions are very conspicuous in the folk medicine of that state. "Its uses are legion", he writes. "Very little inquiry into folk cures is necessary to secure the information that 'onions is healthy'. Eating onions, raw or cooked, will help to cure colds. The juice roasted or fried out of onions, when sweetened with sugar, makes one of the best cough syrups for babies. Onion beaten to a pulp and moistened with kerosene makes a poultice that cures snakebite. The poultice draws out the poison from the bite, as is seen by the green color of the poultice after it has been on the bite a short time. I have noticed that green is a 'poison color' in the folk medicine I have met. Onions may be used to take up 'yaller janders'. The onion is cut into halves and then hung up in the room where a person has the jaundice. The cut surface of the onion takes up the disease from the air. The onion should be replaced by a fresh one when the yellow of the jaundice that has been taken up begins to show on the onion"; and one of the oldest and most popular treatments for croup was a poultice of onion lightly fried.

CEBOLLITA DEL CAMPO

CACOMITE
SAITAS
WILD ONION
GRASSNUT
BLUE DICK
CLUSTER LILY
SPANISH LILY
LILY FAMILY

Allium recurvatum Rydb.

Liliaceæ

Some Spanish-Californians used to call the wild onions *saitas,* but often the name *cacomite* lingered as an Aztec survival in isolated regions of the state. *Cacomitl* is supposed to be the exact word spoken by Montezuma, and was translated by one of the Spanish chroniclers as "wild roots with the flavor of chestnuts".

Its loose clusters of bluish pink flowers topping a slender stalk are a common sight in the lush grasslands of New Mexico, and its bulbs furnish both a food and several remedies to the inhabitants. The wild onion is chewed to relieve flatulency. As a febrifuge it is mashed and soaked in water. This is then strained and drunk. The bulbs may be eaten raw or cooked, especially with meat, and are considered quite palatable and nourishing if consumed in either way.

CHAMISO

CHAMIS   Atriplex canescens Pursh
SALTBUSH
SHAD SCALE
GOOSEFOOT FAMILY   Chenopodiaceæ

The saltbush is one of the commonest shrubs on the plains and in the arroyos and lower valleys of the state, and it is now being planted extensively, under governmental direction, on many areas in the Southwest to increase the growth of range vegetation and decrease soil erosion. One of the leading stockmen in Western New Mexico stated that saltbush "is a godsend in fall and winter" as a forage for sheep and cattle, although it sometimes causes more or less bloat among the sheep in summer, especially after rains.

The Indians, who have developed usages for so many plants, have adapted the *chamiso* to their purposes. On a Hopi mesa, in the village of Hano, the ashes of the saltbush are stirred into the batter of the purplish-gray waferbread in order to change the natural color of the ground meal into a greenish blue, as lime water is used by the Spanish New Mexicans to improve their blue meal porridge. The Zuñi attach prayer plumes to the bush in the belief that this action will bring forth the cottontail rabbit in large numbers.

Nor are the other inhabitants of New Mexico behind the Indians in their reliance upon the saltbush. For at Tularosa the green leaves are chewed with a pinch of salt, followed by a swallow of water, to relieve bad stomach pains.

CHAMISO CIMARRON
CHAMISO BLANCO

GOLDEN BUSH   Chrysothamnus graveolens Nutt.
FALSE GOLDENROD
RABBIT BRUSH
ASTER FAMILY   Compositæ

To any one who knows it intimately, the *chamiso blanco* recalls instantly the all-pervading sense of beauty which one attaches to New Mexico in the early autumn. Nothing so completely characterizes the landscape as the silvery-green foliage and storm of yellow bloom rolling down its washes and across its *lomas* in September.

One is not surprised to hear that from the flowers comes the rich yellow dye that brightens the native blankets. It is one of the oldest known of the indigenous dyes, and furthermore the Spanish-Americans mix *guaco* with the solution from the boiled flowers for a yellow paint.

A tea made from the plant is used as a febrifuge and, finally, its white galls, resulting from the sting of a dipterous insect, are strung as beads and hung around babies' necks. This practice is supposed to stop their drooling.

CHAMISO HEDIONDO

SAGEBRUSH   Artemisia tridentata Nutt.
WORMWOOD   Artemisia bigelovii Gray
ASTER FAMILY   Compositæ

"The Riders of the Purple Sage" and many other books and stories have so closely associated sagebrush with western characteristics that the term is now rather loosely used for more than one kind of desert shrub. Artemisia tridentata is the true sagebrush. It is a social shrub which preempts vast acres and practically drives out ever other similar growth.

The people of Nevada considered it so representative of their state that they adopted sagebrush as their floral emblem,

and so wide is its distribution that nearly every pioneer cross-
ing the United States had to contend with the "everlasting
sagebrush". However, when he set up camp at night it was
often the only fuel he could find, and had he known as much
as some Indians, he might have chewed its leaves to relieve
the gripes and flatulence resulting from meals hastily prepared
and quickly swallowed. Even now at Hano the Tewa Indians
masticate *chamiso hediondo* with water, or drink it in a hot
decoction as a remedy for indigestion, and steep a bundle of
the plants in boiling water, wrap them in a cloth, and apply
them to the stomach as a hot compress.

To the Spanish-American of New Mexico, a large quantity
of its leaves, boiled in water, make an excellent bath for
rheumatism, croup, and pains in the chest and limbs due to
colds. Or a strong tea, brewed from the leaves, taken three
times a day with *piloncillo* (Mexican brown sugar), serves the
same purpose. When suddenly faced with the war-time prob-
lem of curing "flu", they administered a brandy and *chamiso
hediondo* tea, covered the patient's body with ground onions
and pepper, and wrapped him in several blankets until he
perspired profusely. Another remedy for influenza, or for
dropsy, is to boil one dozen pellets of *estiercol de cabra* (goat
manure), in a gallon of water, and drink a glass of the tea in
the morning.

At El Rito, the whole plant is boiled and a bath is given
for colds accompanied by high fevers; and to relieve stomach
pains, the fresh leaves are crushed, strained through a fine
cloth, mixed with luke-warm water, and drunk.

The low-growing variety in Chimayo serves as a hemostatic remedy. A tea is made from the leaves with which the
penitentes bathe their backs after flagellation, and which is
taken internally to stop the flow of blood from their wounds.

CHAN

MINT FAMILY

Salvia reflexa Hornem.
Labiatæ

Chan is the well-known *chía*, whose seeds, in California, were roasted, ground, and used as food. A gruel of these was one of the peace-offerings to the first visiting sailors, and one tablespoonful of the seeds were sufficient to sustain for twenty-four hours an Indian on a forced march. It was prized so highly even in 1894 by the native Californian that he frequently paid six or eight dollars a pound to obtain it. It is quite common throughout California, growing in waste ground and damp fields.

In New Mexico, a bitter decoction of the dry or green leaves is taken to relieve stomach trouble, or the fresh leaves are chewed with a little salt for the same purpose. And for colic, half a teaspoonful of *cal* (lime) and a whole teaspoonful of *chan* are boiled in half a cup of water.

A *chan* seed when placed in the eye is said to remove an offending particle quickly, as linseed relieved our grandmothers.

It is believed by the natives that if they surround their beds with a circle of green *chan*, all the bedbugs will keep respectfully away. But what happens when it is no longer green undoubtedly is a matter for conjecture, unless the winter frosts come to the rescue in time.

CHICO

TOMATILLO
RABBIT THORN
CHICO BUSH
NIGHTSHADE FAMILY

Lycium pallidum—Miers

Solanaceæ

This homely, spiny shrub, with stubby leaves and small red berries, was one of Frémont's discoveries in 1844, although the Spanish residents in our Southwest had already known it and given it the affectionate terms of *tomatillo*, after its berries which greatly resemble a small tomato, and *chico,* little one. Nor had the Indians of this region neglected the existence of this inhabitant of mesas, washes, and arid stony hillsides. According to Dr. Washington Matthews, an army surgeon who lived in their country for many years, the Navajos gave the berries sacred significance. The Zuñi treated them with great reverence as an intercessor with the gods of the harvest, and so their priests would, when the berries appeared upon the bush, sprinkle it with sacred meal, saying the following prayer: "My father, I give you prayer-meal; I want as many peaches as your berries". They also considered that the boiled berries were a real table delicacy.

Among the New Mexicans the red fruit is eaten raw if perfectly ripe, or boiled and consumed as a separate dish or in combination with stews and soups to give them a particular flavor. This *tomatillo* is frequently dried and stored away for winter use.

I have been told that horses or cattle will not touch the *chico,* but that it is fattening fodder for goats and sheep.

CHICÓRIA

ACHICORIA	Taraxacum officinale Web.
ACHICORIA AMARGA	
CONSUELDA	
BLOW BALL	
CANKERWORT	
DANDELION	
ASTER FAMILY	Compositæ

The jagged edge of the irregularly-toothed, deep green leaves of the European species suggested the row of teeth in a lion's jaw, as figured in early woodcuts of herbal times, hence the English name of dandelion, which is a corruption of the French, *dent-de-lion.*

It is not surprising that so common and familiar a weed should be the basis of several foods and remedies in New Mexico. A handful of its flowers are boiled until the water turns very yellow. Then the liquid is allowed to stand out-of-doors all night. A glass must be taken before breakfasting, every morning for a month, to cure heart trouble. The boiled flowers also yield a yellow dye that is used to color deer skins.

The raw or cooked greens, seasoned with a little vinegar, are said to purify the blood; or, with a wine made of the flowers, the same effect is accomplished.

Many children are familiar with the necklaces that can be made from its flower stems, and nearly everyone who has lived in the country during youth has held up the ripened seed heads to see which way the wind was blowing. This practice probably gave rise to the popular name of blow-ball.

At San Ildefonso pueblo, the ground leaves, reduced to a paste with water, are spread over a fracture, and fresh leaves of the same plant are bound on it with rags. In Santa Clara, the pulverized leaves, mixed with dough, are applied to a bad bruise.

CHIQUETE DE EMBARAÑADA
CHICOTE EMBARRAÑADA

ASTER FAMILY

Lygodemia juncea Pursh
Compositæ

In May, small yellow balls form on the plant and the children gather them for gum. But, what is most surprising, these yellow balls turn bright blue when they are chewed, and small boys can spit a nice long blue streamer at the family cat, or sister's clean dress, or perhaps can scare mother a little into thinking they have been eating something perfectly horrible.

CHILE

CHILLI   Capsicum frutescens longum Bailey
CHILI
NIGHTSHADE FAMILY   Solanaceæ

According to Francisci Hernandes and Nardo Antonio Reccho, who published at Rome, in 1651, a copious volume entitled "Rerum Medicarum Novæ Hispaniæ Thesaurus Sev Plantarum Animalium Mineralium Mexicanorum", which fortunately has retained for us much of the medicinal knowledge of the Aztec, there were at least seven varieties of *chile* recognized by these ancient Mexicans, which they considered excellent remedies. These peppers were variously given the names of *quauchilli, milchilli, zenalchilli, tlalchilli, tefochilli, chiltecpin,* and *chilocoztli,* from which our present word is obviously a derivation. With evidently little distinction between the separate forms, they were employed as a purge, as a remedy for inflammation of the kidneys and brain, for lung afflictions, heart pains, very bad blood, diarrhea, and internal tumors. Their value as a nutritive condiment was well known, and they were carefully tended in those elaborate gardens that excited the admiration and respect of the conquering Spaniards.

Nor were the neighbors of the Aztec, the Maya, behind them in utilizing the *chile* as a remedy in combination with other ingredients, as Ralph L. Roys tells us. Their texts prescribed a mixture of the sap of Capsicum axi Vell., often referred to as the *chile colorado* by the Spanish-Americans of New Mexico, with a crystal of salt, which was to be put out in the dew until dawn and then drunk for blood in the stools. The Maya gave the name of *ic,* or *yax-ic,* to Capsicum annuum, and employed it for irritated throat in the following manner: "Let him (the patient) drink cold water when he is taken with it. Take a tomin of honey and half an ounce of Spanish pepper. Grind it and sprinkle it on the honey. Also twelve chile peppers and half a leaf of tobacco, pulverized also. Then let it be put in the honey and boiled until it has boiled away. If

62

there is a chill, you take it cold and put it on the end of his tongue until it is sucked away. Then let him cover himself up and not drink cold water for three days. With this he will recover". And if the afterbirth may have been retarded in part for two days, the postconquest Maya administered grated Jatropha aconitifolia Mill. *(chaya),* with horse dung and honey and Capsicum annuum. "She will recover by this means", they affirmed.

The Capsicum frutescens, called *chile del monte* by the Spanish and *max* and *max-ic* by the Maya, was considered by the latter in the seventeenth century to be excellent for dysentery. "You take ten lemons and squeeze the juice into a gourd", they said. "The add ten peppers of the *Capsicum frutescens,* L., or of Havana chile into the juice of these lemons. Then hang it in the doorway of the house from sunset until dawn, then warm it, and give it to drink."

And the Spanish-Americans of New Mexico have inherited the knowledge that was acquired in old México of *chile* and its cultivation. In March and April they plant its seeds in whatever tins and boxes they may possess, and place them, within the houses, on their broad window-ledges, to germinate. With due regard for the influence of numbers, the last day upon which the young shoots may be transplanted to the open gardens is the third of May. They begin to come to complete fruition about the middle of September; they first develop a glossy green skin and clear white seeds, and as such, they may be picked and cooked or slit open to dry. But if left on the plant a little longer, they turn scarlet, and are then strung in huge festoons and hung on racks or along the house-fronts, to dry in the sun. No matter on what they are suspended, so much compact brilliance is invariably a startling surprise in a region where greys and greens and browns mingle with such little effort.

The Spanish-Americans always have been adept at striking a hard bargain, and will spend several hours of measured argument, during which time they will be thoroughly enjoy-

63

ing themselves. *Chile* is to them what distinguished economists are prone to term an "exchange product". It even approaches a "standard of value", as it is one of the most important crops upon which they can realize a cash return.

Since many of them have not yet reached that greatly desired (or so we are told) and mythical "high standard of living" whereby they can bring their *chile* to town in automobiles or trucks, they merely harness up a pair of horses or mules to their sturdy canvas-hooded carts, pile them high with *ristras* (strings of *chile*) and go from village to village in these smaller versions of the famous "covered wagon", to bargain and perhaps get a little money to buy the *esposa* a new dress, the children some shoes, and a little *mula blanca* (white mule) for themselves.

I am told that *chile colorado,* the red *chile,* will neutralize rheumatism, even if the unfortunate person is "*mucho muy sick*". One red pepper is split open and soaked in warm vinegar for twenty-four hours. Then a cloth is steeped in the liquid and applied to the afflicted part. This compress is kept moist until the pain departs.

Should one suffer from swollen glands in the region of the throat, the red *chile* is boiled and tied on to relieve the distress. In the event that one has a tumor in his fingers or toes, if he will simply immerse a *chile* in hot water, open it, and wrap it around the diseased part, replacing the old pepper every day with a fresh one similarly prepared—allegedly, it will draw out the pus.

During the summer the persistent and tenacious *chinches* (bedbugs) sometimes become so annoying that their probings have to be curbed, and so the *chile* seeds and veins are burned as a fumigant.

If you are so unfortunate as to become a victim of *brujería* (witchcraft), you may tie two good-sized nails in the shape of a cross with a piece of wire, put this in the fire, and when it is redhot place thereon a small string of "hearts of *chile*", then sprinkle over the whole some Mexican rock salt with a motion describing the cross, and add a little kerosene; the resultant flame is intended to burn up all the witchery that may have threatened you.

CHILE PUERCO

PIGWEED
AMARANTH FAMILY

Amaranthus blitoides S. Wats
Amaranthaceæ

Chile puerco seeds were an important item in the ancient Zuñi menu. They believed that the original seeds were brought up from the undermost world at the time of the tribe's emergence on the surface of the earth, and scattered by the rain priests. But after the corn maiden gave them corn, the pigweed seeds were mixed with it. And even now, an admixture of black corn meal and *chile puerco* seeds is made into balls or pats, laid on a rack of sticks or slats, and steamed for several hours.

When young, the leaves are gathered by the New Mexicans for greens, and in the spring, the Tewa Indians also boil and fry them.

The plant can be crushed, water added, and the liquid used as a face wash to bleach the skin after it has been sunburnt.

It is said that it is very good for fattening pigs, as are the other amaranths, and for this reason the popular name of pigweed has been indiscriminately applied to them all.

CHIMAJÁ

PARSLEY FAMILY

Aulospermum purpureum S. Wats.
Umbelliferæ

The *chimajá* is a most deceptive plant, for one would little suspect on looking at its insignificant proportions and small yellow flower that beneath them a very large root had wormed its way far beneath the soil in search of moisture. But the children of Peña Blanca know it well, and dig up these roots and eat them raw; and for the early settlers it constituted an important article of their diet. In olden days, every bar in the region was graced by a bottle of whiskey containing *chimajá*, and at Los Lunas, its flowers, with sugar, were added to a stone jug of whiskey, and allowed to stand for two years. This made an excellent cordial called *mestela*, which was served in tiny glasses at *fiestas* and other celebrations.

Furthermore, the dry leaves and flowers are boiled and a wine glass of the tepid tea is taken three times a day for debility, and stomach trouble.

Early in the spring, its leaves are picked and kept to season dry, or green, beans, and even peas.

CLAVELINA
CLAVELLINA

MY LADY'S WASH-BOWL   Saponaria officinalis L.
COW HERB
DOG CLOVES
BOUNCING BET
WHEAT COCKLE
SOAPWORT
WILD SOAPWORT
PINK FAMILY   Caryophyllaceæ

Bouncing Bet was not a native-born American, but she could doubtless qualify for the Daughters of the American Revolution, as she came over very early and is now a buxom lass hiding her charms in the corners of many old-fashioned gardens, or near the settlements of men. She is known as *clavelina* in Spanish, and the same plant is sometimes called Julián at Chimayo, where it is kept in a bowl inside the houses, as the people say, "to scare off the flies".

While calling at Sile, I was very annoyed by the large number of flies in the room, and remarked that the Almighty, who had given everything some useful purpose, had forgotten to do so when He created the fly. "Oh, no", my hostess objected, "they are very good for corns and callouses. You make

66

a *clastico de mosca,* a poultice from the squashed flies and apply".

The former usage of *clavelina* roots as a soap appears to have nearly died out, for now many of the people who have it in their gardens don't realize that a good lather is produced when the roots are agitated in water.

COLITA DE RATA
COLITA DE RATÓN

BUCKWHEAT FAMILY

Eriogonum racemosum Nutt.
Polygonaceæ

People are not alone in receiving nicknames because of some noticeable feature or mannerism, for many plants have so striking a character that they, too, are given names by those who live with them. And so startling was the resemblance, that the Spanish-Americans of New Mexico have called this plant Rat's-tail.

An old authority informed me that its stems are to be recommended for cleaning the teeth, as this treatment keeps them in good condition.

CONTRAYERBA

CALTROP
CALTROP FAMILY

Kallstrœmia brachystylis Vail
Zygophyllaceæ

*Contrayerb*a is a trailing, slightly hairy herb with axillary orange flowers, opposite leaves, and a spiny fruit, which grows on the dry plains in the lower and upper Sonoran zones of New Mexico. It is not the same plant that was formerly called *contrayerba* and used by the Spaniards in Perú as an antidote against poison, and which was introduced into England in 1581 under the name of Drakesfoot, one year after Sir Francis Drake successfully completed his circumnavigation of the globe.

67

Spanish New Mexicans say that the powdered caltrop's roots, soaked in warm water, make a good wash for sore eyes and swollen gums; and, if taken as a tea, form an excellent remedy for fever, stomach trouble, and dysentery. They also employ a combination of ground *calabazilla* flowers (wild gourd), *alverjon de patito* (peas of Lathyrus decaphyllus), and powdered *contrayerba* roots, to rub on the face under the eyes for pains in that region. If caltrop is mixed in equal parts with *oshá* (Ligusticum porteri), and *copalquin* (Peruvian red bark), and boiled, the ensuing compound tea will relieve diarrhea.

The Indians of San Ildefonso pueblo evidently have had use for *contrayerba* similar to those of the New Mexican Spaniards, as they chew the leaves and put them on sores or swellings, and drink a decoction of the roots for diarrhea.

CORALILLO

KINNIKINNIC   Arctostaphylos uva-ursi (L.) Spreng.
MANZANITA (Californian Spanish)
RED BEARBERRY
BEARBERRY
ARBERRY
UPLAND CRANBERRY
HEATH FAMILY   Ericaceæ

Coralillo, a low perennial shrub with leathery leaves, which grows in mountain regions, contains a certain amount of tannic acid which gives it astringent and curative properties.

The Indians and early settlers found *coralillo* a substitute for real tobacco. It was pulverized and carried in leather pouches, and known in many dialects as *k'nick k'nack*. But the Pueblo Indians of the Río Grande number its leaves among the varieties dried and smoked in their "cloud-blowers", or straight cylindrical pipes used only in ceremonial smoking.

It is also recommended in the treatment of syphilis and gonorrhea. The plant is boiled in water and *piloncillo* is added. A cup of the liquid is heated and drunk every morning for ten days. As a tea it is taken to reduce fat, and one may bathe in a decoction of it for rheumatism. Its somewhat involved botanical name, as is so often the case, is a combination of Greek and Latin words: the Greek *arktos,* bear, and *staphyle,* grape; and the Latin, *uva,* cluster, and *ursus,* bear.

The "mata" (that portion of the plant above ground) is boiled and the resultant tea is drunk every morning before breakfast for "cold blood" (anæmia) or stomach trouble.

CORONILLA

YERBA DEL SOL (Galisteo)　　　　Gaillardia pinnatifida Torr.
BLANKET FLOWER
ASTER FAMILY　　　　　　　　　Compositæ

The *coronilla* (little crown) was given its Latin name after Gaillard de Marentonneau, the French botanist.

Its golden, yellow-rayed flowers, with a center of shaded maroon, are supported by a thin hairy stalk about a foot tall, bearing stiff dull-green leaves. When the rays drop off, a fuzzy, globular seed-container is exposed.

According to an old Tesuque *médica,* women who want children wash and boil the whole plant, with the exception of the flower, add *piloncillo* (brown sugar) and strain the whole decoction. One glass, luke-warm, is drunk three times a day before meals.

And at Galisteo, the stems without leaves are mashed for a cold and a pain in the head. A little salt and water are added, and this is applied to the forehead or temples.

The Navajo Indians use the plant to resuscitate those who are in danger of dying from drowning.

It is also taken generally for anæmia.

There is another variety, somewhat taller and with yellow flowers, that is called *hilotito* in Galisteo, where it is considered a remedy for headache. It is ground into a fine powder and rubbed on the temples and forehead, and a pinch of the powder is snuffed up the nose so that the pain will leave at once.

COTA
TE SILVESTRE

WILD TEA

ASTER FAMILY

Thelesperma gracile A. Gray
Thelesperma longipes A. Gray
Compositæ

Before tea or coffee were imported into New Mexico, *cota* was used widely as a beverage; and even now, in the more isolated communities, it serves this purpose. Furthermore, with two tablespoonsful of sugar, a very strong decoction is taken to reduce fever. When babies' skins become chafed, they are bathed in a weak solution, and given a little to drink.

One Sunday several years ago, lunching in Santo Domingo pueblo, I noticed that several small bundles of it, hung on corn husk loops, were suspended from the *vigas* inside the house. As soon as I called attention to them, my Indian host replied, "Oh, yes, tea for the *estomago* (stomach). It is very good", he continued, "because it cleans you all out".

Should one wish a diuretic, *cota* tea may be drunk nine days in succession. It is also an excellent vermifuge.

Since the tea is reddish-brown, it was formerly used as a dye to color "the stems of rabbitbrush for the patterns of the wicker plaques of the Moki Indians of Northern Arizona", says Walter Hough.

A yellow dye is also made from its flowers.

CRISANTA
CRISANTEMO

CHYSANTHEMUM
ASTER FAMILY

Chrysanthemum indicum L.
Compositæ

In New Mexico, as in ancient China and elsewhere, the greatly-appreciated and hardy chrysanthemum is always carefully tended, that its colorful clusters may illumine gardens made somewhat bare by the passing of many other flowers.

70

At La Bajada it is taken for relief from stomach ache. The leaf may be chewed and ejected, or swallowed; or a tea can be made with it and drunk.

CUAJO

RENNET

While concluding negotiations for the purchase of some property near Santa Fé, I noticed that the owner's finger was badly cut, and asked how it had happened. He explained the wound came from the rusty wire of a hay-baler. I was deeply alarmed, fearing that blood poisoning might result if his finger did not receive proper attention, and when I saw him again a few days later, an infection had spread to his shoulder. I asked him how it had been treated, and he told me with *cañaigre*. This naturally closed the only normal bodily outlet, resulting in angry pustules all over his arm. I was afraid he might die, and advised his visiting a physician in town. With scorn he replied, "We never had doctors in the old days", and resolutely refused my suggestion. A week later, I had to see him again, and dreading I might find my man in his grave, I was amazed as he appeared with a cheerful smile, and seemed in the best of health. Then he said that upon the advice of a friend, he had tied rennet on his hand, and boastingly declared that he was practically well.

Mi amigo, he continued, once stepped on a long rusty nail which entered his heel, and soon poisoned him so badly that his entire leg was streaked with red. But he had bound rennet on the primary wound and it drew out all the poison. He lost only the flesh surrounding the puncture, and was soon completely cured.

CUERO

Cuero literally means leather of all kinds, but here we are concerned only with the hide from a black cow. It appears that in every cow of this color there is a potential remedy against excessive mensis, and the cure can only be achieved through the most strict compliance with the following directions: First remove the black hair from the hide, and cut it into strips. These are to be roasted in the oven until they are the color of coffee, care being taken to watch them closely lest they turn black. Then you grind them very fine and put the powder through a sieve. Next, you mix a tablespoonful of the substance with a capsule of quinine in a glass of water, and take it thrice daily. The cure can only be completed by washing the parts with *yerbabuena* tea (spearmint), and then applying a hot cloth which has been spread with castor oil and mentholatum.

CUIPA DE SABINA
(Juniper Bark)

COMMON CEDAR
CYPRESS FAMILY

Juniperus sp.
Cupressaceæ

It is a common fault among people of limited experience with evergreens to refer to junipers as "cedars", whereas there are really no true cedars native to the United States.

Both the Zuñi and Tewa Indians use the bark of juniper as a tinder and kindling material.

New Mexican *médicas* are sometimes called upon to cure *hervor de sangre* (skin rash presumably caused by high blood pressure). When this occasion arises, they boil two heaping handsful of *cuipa de sabina* in a quart of water, strain the liquid when it has cooled, and add a teaspoonful of soda and a tablespoonful of salt. They sponge the entire body of the patient with this solution, and prescribe a complete rest until the itching, through this treatment, has disappeared.

CULANTRO
CILANTRO

CORIANDRO (Castilian)   Coriandrum sativum L.
CORIANDER
PARSLEY FAMILY   Umbelliferæ

This is the common coriander of the gardens, the seed of which is so extensively used as flavoring, and which occurs occasionally in waste ground, having escaped from the confines of garden walls. On account of its pleasant and pungent flavor it is a favorite ingredient in hot curries and sauces, and in medicine it is a carminiative and aromatic.

Culantro is a native of southern Europe and Asia Minor, and, among other plants which still can be found growing amid Roman ruins, was introduced into England by the Romans. A fascinating quarto, entitled "Historie of Plantes", compiled by Dodœns, and published at London in 1578, reveals that the people of the British Isles employed coriander seeds in the following manner during the sixteenth century: "Coriander seeds prepared, and taken alone (or couered in Sugar) after meales, closeth up the mouth of the stomache, stayeth vomiting, and helpeth digestion. The same roasted or parched and drunke with wine, killeth and bringeth foorth wormes of the body, and stoppeth the bloudy flow and all other extraordinarie issues of bloud". The same volume states that "this herb is called in Latine and in Shoppes *Coriandrum,* in English *coriander,* and of some *Coliader,* in Italian *Coriandro,* in French *Coriandre,* in Douch *Coriander,* and in Spanish *Coentro, Culantro*". Thus we find that the Spanish New Mexicans have preserved in their present speech the sixteenth-century word *culantro,* brought to them from Spain by the intrepid *conquistadores* who were beginning to extend their explorations into the American Southwest when our reference book was written.

Without being at all inconsistent with medieval usages, the Spanish descendants in New Mexico now consider cori-

73

ander seeds an excellent relish. They mix them with *yerba-buena* (spearmint), *oregano* (monarda), marjoram, and *chile,* to make a sauce for kid stew. Their remedy for pyorrhea and toothache is a simple one: Some *culantro* is boiled in water, and the hot liquid is held in the mouth. A similar decoction of the plant, although somewhat stronger, is taken as often as necessary by those who are suffering from "cold in the stomach".

For headache they cover the head, lean over live coals on which have been sprinkled a few grains of *culantro,* and inhale the fumes.

If, by some visitation of a not altogether divine providence, your chickens should have a cold, a few *culantro* seeds "will cure them in no time".

DORMILÓN

TALL CONE FLOWER   Rudbeckia laciniata L.
ASTER FAMILY   Compositæ

Since nearly everyone in New Mexico has an astounding number of *primos,* cousins, it is not surprising that the plants also should be provided with relationships. The familiar sunflower and common black-eyed Susan can look with favor upon the *dormilón* as really one of the family, for it is their first cousin.

It was given its Latin name nearly two centuries ago by Linnæus, who dedicated it to Olaus Rudbeck, father and son, distinguished instructors at the University of Upsala. Linnæus studied there under Olaus *fils,* then an old man, and lived in his house for a time tutoring two young Rudbecks.

The Spanish-Americans of New Mexico say that this *dormilón* is a good remedy for gonorrhea. Enough of its dry or green leaves to make a strong tea are boiled in a quart or two of water. This is then strained, a little *piloncillo* is added,

74

and a cup is drunk every morning. Exactly the same preparation, taken every morning for nine days as an emmenagogue for female trouble.

DORMILÓN

CONE FLOWER
ASTER FAMILY

Rudbeckia tagetes James
Compositæ

Evidently even the New Mexicans felt that *dormilón* itself should have a *primo,* for they also give the species Rudbeckia tagetes the same name.

It, too, is used for female trouble, but in a somewhat different manner. When congestion sets in with a cold, the wet roots are crushed, or the dry roots ground, and one teaspoonful is mixed with a glass of cold water. Then this is taken three times a day. My specimen was collected at an altitude of 8,000 feet above sea-level, at Truchas.

VERVENA
DORMILÓN

Verbena macdougalii Heller
Verbenaceæ

VERVAIN FAMILY

The other two flowers that are called *dormilón,* meaning sleepy-head, are yellow, but this variety is purple, and is more often referred to as *vervena.*

Children apparently take the keenest pleasure in inflicting minor injuries upon their playmates; the New Mexican boys have found that one of the easiest methods of accomplishing this is by striking an unsuspecting companion on the bare legs with a whip of *vervena.* With this, it won't be long before he becomes sufficiently angry for all purposes of amusement. The plant evidently has some irritating hairs that penetrate the flesh aside from the actual impact of the blows, and is therefore particularly fine for rousing the fury of one's companions.

As a diuretic, a tea of the *vervena* is drunk for nine mornings; and, at Mora, for toothache, the green leaves are mashed and placed inside the mouth on the gums and on the cheek.

When not speaking of plants, the use of the name *dormilón* applies to a bat, and I have heard some of the native children call the black, strong-smelling beetle "sleepy-head," or *dormilón,* because he so frequently puts his head to the ground, though his rightful name in this area is *perrodo,* and less commonly, *pinacate*.

DURAZNO

PEACH   Prunus persica (L.) Sieb & Zucc.
ALMOND FAMILY   Drupaceæ

Although it is obvious that there are a great many varieties of peach trees, they are usually designated as Prunus persica unless a more specific identification is required.

There is a wide divergence of opinion about the origin of the peach, one group attributing it to China, while the other (especially championed by Charles Darwin) looks upon it as a modification of the almond. Nevertheless, it is a matter of record that the peach was designated as *to* or *tao* by Confucius in the fifth century before Christ, and even appeared in other Chinese writings dating from the tenth century before the Christian era.

We are indebted to the Arabs for many of our delicious syrups, sherbets and juleps, and the fragrant flavoring waters and conserves of scented flowers. According to the tales of the Arabian nights, these people prepared a peach syrup by soaking the blossoms in warm water for a day, and then repeating the infusion with fresh flowers four times. This was strained, two pounds of sugar, preferably in a single lump, were allowed for each pint of liquid, and the entire preparation was boiled until it poured like oil.

At present, in Morocco, there is a saying, "If the peaches could cure anybody, they would have cured themselves", and

76

it is used by a man who has been asked to intervene on another's behalf.

Culpeper writes of this fruit: "For children and young people nothing is better to purge choler and the jaundice, than the leaves of flowers being made into a syrup or conserve . . . The flowers steeped all night in a little warm wine, strained in the morning, and drunk fasting, gently opens the belly, and purges".

Evidently this use has been continued in New Mexico, for the flowers are regarded as a good purge even now by its Spanish Americans.

At Tularosa, the *cascara de durazno* (peach bark), is boiled in water and taken as a hot or cold tea to reduce high fever.

But the peach leaves *(hojas de durazno)* are the portion of the tree from which the greatest number of remedies are derived. A tea is made from them for asthma and as an expectorant; and it is valued as a general tonic. Taken as a hot douche, the decoction is said to relieve menstrual troubles.

"The Housekeeper's Manual", published in Nashville, January 1, 1875, gives us a practical recipe for peach-leaf yeast. "Hops cost two dollars per pound, leaves cost nothing, and peach leaves make better yeast than hops. Thus: Take three handfuls of peach leaves, and three medium-sized potatoes; boil them in two quarts of water until the potatoes are done; take out the leaves and throw them away; peel the potatoes and rub them up with a pint of flour, adding cool water sufficient to make a paste; then pour on the hot peach-leaf tea, and scald for about five minutes. If you add to this a little old yeast, it will be ready for use in three hours; if you add none, it will require to stand a day and night before use. Leaves dried in the shade are as good as fresh ones. As this is stronger than hop yeast, less should be used in making up the dough".

ENCINILLO

FENDLER OAK   Quercus fendleri Liebm.
BEECH FAMILY   Fagaceæ

Of all the nuts that nature has given us, and which we have disregarded, except for fattening hogs, the most outstanding is the acorn. Certain groups of Indians have seriously utilized them for human consumption, and it is significant that among the fattest of all the Indians, the Californians, acorn meal has been a staple diet with them since prehistoric times.

The *bellotas,* or acorns produced by this variety of oak, are ravenously devoured by the bears of New Mexico, but the Spanish-Americans there, rather than include it in their diet, make only a tea from the leaves, fresh or dry, to give strength to the blood, or drink it cold for anæmia.

ENCINO
ENCINO DE LA HOJA ANCHA

GAMBELL'S SCRUB OAK   Quercus gambelii Nutt.
BEECH FAMILY   Fagaceæ

Stephen Powers, in his estimable work on "The Tribes of California", writes that so important an element as the acorn in their tribal life became associated with religious ceremonial and was incorporated into native poetry, and their autumn gathering of the nuts was celebrated with dances and songs of thanksgiving, of which the following is one:

> *"The acorns come down from heaven;*
> *I plant the short acorns in the valley;*
> *I plant the long acorns in the valley;*
> *I sprout, I, the black acorn sprout;*
> *I sprout".*

The descendants of the *conquistadores* in New Mexico say

78

that their *encino* furnishes the necessary materials for the successful treatment of any kind of sores, and for external cancer. The branches are boiled, and the lotion, when lukewarm, is applied to the sores. When this has been done, they are sprinkled with the powdered bark, and bandaged. The lotion heals and the powder is drying. For malaria, the *cascara* (bark) is boiled in water and the tea is allowed to stand overnight in a window. At sunrise, a glass is drunk. This is repeated in the mornings only; and, at Mora, the same treatment is taken to cure diarrhea. I was also told at Mora that should one have a felon on the thumb, constant bathing in the tepid tea is the only thing to do.

It is common knowledge that the Europeans have long made yellow dyes from oak bark, and that they have also relied upon it in tanning their hides. But they may not have discovered the trick that a calculating Moroccan told me. "If you powder a certain part of the bark", he said, "and add it to a tub where hides are soaking in brine, after a month it will have caused the leather to thicken so that it can be sold to greater advantage".

ENTRAÑA

VELAS DE COYOTE   Opuntia arborescens Engelm.
PITAJAYA
TREE CACTUS
CHOYA
CHOLLA
CHANDELIER CACTUS
CANE CACTUS
CANDLE CACTUS
CANDELABRUM CACTUS
CACTUS FAMILY   Cactaceæ

One unfortunate woman, seeking an appropriate name for her ranch among the wealth of Spanish words, finally decided upon *entraña* as an ideal title because she found a plant of this cactus growing on her adobe roof. But later, to her chagrin, she discovered that in English this descriptive name meant entrails!

The word cactus is taken from the Greek, *kaktos,* meaning prickly plant, but the *entraña* is distinguished from the numerous varieties of prickly pear by its upstanding, erect stems, which when completely dried, resemble a cylindrical piece of lattice work. These are sometimes gathered for canes, picture frames, or as souvenirs; and this probably accounts for its being called cane cactus.

After a particularly bad forage year, ranchers burn off its spines so that their stock may feed on the green stalks.

New Mexicans sometimes use it as a hair tonic. The roots are soaked in cold water for three or four days. Then, to check falling hair and to stimulate growth, the head is first shampooed and afterward rinsed with the infusion.

Finally, the brilliant magenta flowers are made into a tea and taken as a diuretic.

ESCOBA DE LA VÍBORA
YERBA DE LA VÍBORA
COLLÁLLE

YELLOW WEED   Gutierrezia tenuis Greene
BROWN WEED
DROPSEED GRASS
SHEEP WEED
SNAKE WEED
RATTLESNAKE WEED
RATTLESNAKE ROOT
RATTLESNAKE MASTER
ASTER FAMILY   Compositæ

A multitude of wild plants have, at various times and in all parts of the United States, had a place in popular favor as remedies more or less efficacious for the bites of poisonous serpents, and have therefore been the recipients of several of the English names given above. The *escoba de la víbora,* meaning broom of the viper, has also been similarly designated by the English-speaking population of the Southwest, although the application of such pseudonyms to this plant appears to be based upon a translation of its Spanish name, rather than upon any general usage of it as a remedy against snake-bite. When I inquired about the reason for calling it *escoba de la víbora,* I was told that if the entire plant is gathered and held in one's hand, it resembles a broom, but no explanation was forthcoming to throw light upon its association with a snake.

However, in old California, strong *escoba* tea was administered after a tourniquet had been tied above the bite and an incision had been made deep enough so that the blood flowed freely when some one had been struck by a rattlesnake.

Another method which is used by the people around Santa Fé to counteract rattlesnake poison is to slit a live chicken between the breast-bone and wish-bone, and place this slit over an incision made in the wound. When the comb of the chicken turns blue, it is a sign that the chicken is absorbing the poison. At the death of the fowl, another one is used in the same manner and the treatment is continued until the last bird survives. It takes about three chickens to effect a cure, and the white meat is the chief factor. This practice has evolved from the old Indian one of applying any bird in the same manner.

The Spanish-Americans of New Mexico have found that *escoba de la víbora* made an excellent herb for many purposes. For counteracting rheumatism, they make a tea from it, and bathe in the decoction every day for nine days. Or they boil two handsful of the plant, either green or dry, in a gallon of water, strain the liquid, and add half a pint of honey. This mixture is allowed to stand for twenty-four hours; then a glass of it is taken for nine mornings before breakfast.

One *médica* in Arroyo Seco told me of a remedy that had cured a patient "who had suffered from piles for twenty years". She bathed the sores with a decoction of the plant, and applied a little Mexican oil, *aceite mexicano,* to prevent itching. "He never had any more trouble", she proudly concluded. Still another method is to mix ground *collálle* with *añil del muerto,* mentholatum and cigarette ashes and apply. And to prevent the return forever of hemorrhoids, the burned, ground bones of a burro are added to the above preparation, and applied.

Moreover, it is considered a good menostatic. When the flowers are in bloom, they are gathered, mashed well, and forced through a fine cloth to strain off any little sticks. *Romerillo* is also crushed, mixed with the *collálle,* and, with honey, formed into suppositories, which are placed in the vagina and allowed to remain over night. For four mornings a douche is administered, made of the boiled stems of *collálle.* In order to secure success, the patient must eat a small quantity of mint followed by a glass of water before each meal and on retiring.

For womb trouble, dry *collálle* is powdered and mixed in equal parts with powdered *manzanilla* flowers (camomile), powdered *yerbabuena* (spearmint), powdered leaves and flowers of *altamisa mexicana* (feverfew), and a small proportion of *yerba del lobo* (Petalostemum purpureum Rydb.). Then, the directions say, married women (who must remain in bed) mix a pinch in vaseline and use.

The greens, with or without flowers, are boiled as a decoction for stomach ache, and a bath is taken in the same liquid to aid in the recovery from malaria.

ESTAFIATE

AGENJO   Artemisia mexicana Willd.
AGENJO DEL PAIS
AGENJO OFICINAL
WORMWOOD
ROCKY MOUNTAIN SAGE
BLACK SAGE
ASTER FAMILY   Compositæ

Although *estafiate* is the New Spanish term given rather loosely to several artemisias, the Artemisia mexicana appears to be the most generally accepted recipient of the name. Like many other local words, *estafiate* is a mutilated survival of the speech of the ancient Aztecs, who called the same plant *yztau-hiatl.*

The Maya, who referred to it as *zizim,* evidently considered it a very healing herb, since their texts prescribe it for many remedies. As Ralph Roys tells us, a hot application of the boiled plant was used for pleurisy, and its decoction taken for coughs, asthma, and diarrhea. The plant was poulticed on the abdomen for colic, and mixed with maiz-paste (corn mush), it was bound on the heart for vertigo.

Doubtless these former uses were never forgotten, because I have discovered that *estafiate* is still regarded as an excellent cure for diarrhea, dysentery, and intestinal obstructions, in old México. And in old California, it was employed as a stimulant, anthelmintic, and emmenagogue.

Moreover, New Mexico seems to have retained some of the ancient knowledge of its utility. Babies suffering from diarrhea and vomiting are given a tea of this plant by spoonsful, as a purge.

When children are afflicted with coughs and phlegm, the plant is mashed and a little water is added. Then this is tied in a small rag and given them to suck. The older people prepare a bath with it for rheumatism, and commonly drink a tea made with the plant to give relief from stomach-ache or pain in the side.

ESTRELLA DEL NORTE

ZARZA   Echinocystis lobata Torrey & Grey
WILD CUCUMBER
BIG ROOT
GOURD FAMILY   Cucurbitaceæ

The wild cucumber is a social climber and cares little on whom it rises and entangles itself, but it also has good points to recommend it, for it drapes unsightly stumps and varies the general green foliage of thickets and brushy banks of streams with its clusters of white flowers and ball-like fruit hanging by their tails. Its large roots, however, are very bit-

83

ter to the taste and caused a Dr. Albert Kellog, who published the first description of this vine, to give the genus the name of Marah, the significance of which, said he, "would be better understood by perusing Exodus XV 22-26." This passage tells us, "And when they came to Marah, they could not drink of the waters of Marah, for they were bitter."

The dark seeds that are enclosed within their protecting spiny pepos are mottled and colored, with the result that Spanish-Californian children often gathered them for various games. *Zarza* is a Spanish name generally descriptive of all vines in this region, and is more frequently used for this one than its rare but more graceful name of *estrella del norte* (star of the north). A Taos Indian informed me that the green fruit is baked, split open and bound on the afflicted members for rheumatism.

One variety of wild cucumber that grows on garden hedges in Morocco is given the name of "cold fire", and is there employed in making a seton. The leaves are tied on the skin overnight. In the morning the blister which they have formed is opened and a chickpea is inserted.

So many remedies in New Mexico have come from Morocco that doubtless further investigation would reveal more striking similarities between New Mexican and Moroccan usages of the wild cucumber.

FLOR DE SAN JUAN

TREE PRIMROSE
SCURVISH
SCABBISH
KINGS CUREALL
NIGHTWILLOW HERB
EVENING PRIMROSE
EVENING PRIMROSE FAMILY

Anogra runcinata (Engelm.) Woot. & Standl.

Onagraceæ

This primrose is a bashful, fly-by-night flower, for like the owl it scorns the brilliance of daylight, and first blooms under the protecting shelter of evening darkness.

The Spanish New Mexicans say that a decoction of this

primrose counteracts kidney trouble. They prepare it by boiling a tablespoonful of fresh or dry flowers in half a pint of water, and drink it with the addition of a little sugar.

For inflamed throat or tonsil trouble, another method is employed: The fresh flowers are crushed and made into a paste with a little water; this is spread between two pieces of cloth and placed on the throat. The remedy burns like mustard, and has to be removed after a few minutes, but its counterirritant action is said to be very effective.

Not only will its petals allegedly cure freckles when rubbed on the discolored skin, but they will also prevent any recurrence of such pigmentation for the rest of the patient's life. Anyway, so it used to be, the *médicas* tell us, and "what once was, now is".

FLOR DE SANTA RITA

VARAS DE SAN JOSÉ (Tesuque) Castilleja integra A. Gray
YERBA DE APACHE (Cañada de   Castilleja linariæfolia
 los Alamos)
YERBA DE LA MIEL VIRGEN
PAINTER'S BRUSH
INDIAN PAINT BRUSH
PAINTED CUP
FIGWORT FAMILY   Scrophulariaceæ

The *castillejas* form a group of flowers whose nomenclature several botanists appear to have selected as the particular object upon which to fasten their separate views on terminology, with the result that there now exists a great deal of controversy over their correct identifications. A few varieties are indigenous to Latin America, and two of these, natives of Colombia, were the basis upon which the genus was founded by the Spanish botanist Dr. José Celestino Mutis. Dr. Mutis, a century and a half ago, went to New Granada (the Republic of Colombia) as physician to the Viceroy, and died at Santa Fé de Bogotá in 1809. However, he named this group Castilleja, as a compliment to one Castillejo, a botanist of Cadiz.

This paint brush is something of a sham, for it clothes

really insignificant flowers with brilliant bracts; and it is also something of a pickpocket, as its roots often fasten themselves upon neighboring tubers and extract some of their nourishment. Since the painter's brush has a perfectly good root system itself, such conduct is unnecessary, but its ultimate punishment may arrive if it becomes a complete parasite.

The red flower of Castilleja linariæfolia is used as a decoction on the pottery and carved wood produced by the Tewa Indians at Hano. The Zuñi use the root of Castilleja integra in conjunction with the minerals for coloring deerskin black.

As a diuretic, the Spanish New Mexicans wash and boil the plant well. A teaspoonful of sugar is added to the strained liquid, and this is drunk every two or three hours. And for inflammations of the skin and supposed cases of leprosy, two parts of ground *flor de Santa Rita* are mixed with one part of mashed *caña agria* roots (wild pieplant), and one part of powdered *piedra lumbre* (alum). Then this combination is sprinkled on the diseased places as a desiccant.

Children pull off the flowers and suck their honey, in the same way as they extract honey from clover and honeysuckle, and when they hit the back of their hands with painter's brush blossoms, there is a resultant pop like that of small paper bags that have been blown up with air.

FLOR DE SAUZ
CAPULÍN SILVESTRE

ELDERBERRY   Sambucus mexicana Presl.
HONEYSUCKLE FAMILY   Caprifoliaceæ

For nearly as long as there has been a language and alphabets to record it, and a *materia medica* to include it, the elderberry has relieved the ills of mankind. One of the earliest Egyptian papyri, which was found with the bones of a mummy in the Theban Necropolis, contained seven hundred remedies in use during the period of Egypt's greatest civilization. This medicinal treatise highly recommended the elderberry. And the Arabs, to whom we owe so much for their preservation of early Christian medical knowledge, have retained for us, in the "Arabian Nights", a recipe for elderberry, from which they made a *rob*. *Rob* is the Arabic for dense, and, in English, it means a thick fruit syrup which has been made by slowly boiling fruit juice until a great deal of its water content has evaporated. Story-telling was the Arab's highest form of entertainment, and in the famous Al Mansur hospital at Cairo tales were told at night to the sleepless patients, or they were soothed with syrups and conserves, and lulled to slumber with soft music.

According to German folklore, the hat must be doffed in the presence of the elder-tree, and it may be for this reason that a Dr. Boerhaave, 1668-1738, famous Dutch physician, held *Sambucus* in such reverence for the multitude of its virtues that he removed his hat whenever he passed the shrub. And in certain of the districts in the English Midlands, it was believed that the cross of Christ was made with its wood, and therefore it should not be burned as a fuel or treated with disrespect. But there was another common medieval tradition that this was the tree upon which Judas hanged himself, and probably for this reason to be crowned with elder was, in olden times, accounted by some a disgrace.

The *Sambucus* was well-known in old México, and with surprising similarity to the Arabic use, was employed in making *rob de sauco* as a purge. Very small quantities were given, however, for the effects of a large amount were the same as an overdose of a narcotic. The pith and leaves were applied as a cataplasm for hemorrhoids, and its dried flowers were considered excellent for colds, bronchitis, and inflammations of the throat, and were also made into a sudorific.

There are few middle-aged women in America who fail to remember when elder flowers steeped in buttermilk were universally esteemed as a complexion clarifier.

Among the Indians of California, the elder was the "tree of music", and flutes were made of the straight young stems in the springtime, because then its soft pith could be removed easily. Dr. C. Hart Merriam, in his volume, "The Dawn of the World", gives the following legend of one of the Sacramento Valley tribes, explaining how the elder came to be distributed from British Columbia to México: In the beginning there was only one elder tree, that grew far away to the east toward the rising sun in a den of rattlesnakes, and as the wind swayed its branches they sang together day and night to the two women of the star people that watched over it. Now there was one Wek-Wek, the Falcon, grandson of Coyote-man who made the world, who had heard its music and wanted to possess the tree. So he journeyed to its home, and after many importunities persuaded these two heavenly ladies to part with some of its root, that from it many cuttings could be made and all the world could hear its melodies. The old Indians say that in some parts of the country there are still such trees to be found that give off sweet music at night— if one should listen very carefully, for so it used to be.

Nor do the soothing effects of so remarkable a tree pass unnoticed in New Mexico, where the dry flowers act as a febrifuge. Two teaspoonsful of them are allowed to stand in a quart of water for twenty-four hours, after which it is taken a glassful at a time, until the fever has abated. Moreover, if one pours boiling water on the dry flowers, covers them, and allows them to brew, and then adds this mixture to medicate the bath of a paralytic, he will find relief. Many households have long congratulated themselves on their elderberry wine, for which the preparation becomes an important seasonal event, and one *paisano* who lived high on Cumbres Pass enthusiastically declared that the berries of the *capulín silvestre* were even good for fattening chickens.

FRIJOLES

PINTO BEANS   Phaseolus vulgaris L.
PEA FAMILY   Leguminoasæ

Frijoles are to the Spanish-American and Indian of the Southwest what rice is to the Oriental. And besides being one of the most important foods here, this, often the only one that whole families can afford, therefore is a true "staff of life" in the strictest interpretation of that old phrase. *Frijoles* were brought in by the *conquistadores,* and although the Indians knew other beans before the invasion, they have adopted the Spanish varieties almost as completely as their introductors.

Moreover, the plant has other functions besides furnishing an inexpensive and nutritious vegetable. Its green leaves are soaked in one part vinegar and one part cold water, and bound on the forehead and the nape of the neck, to aid in recovery from headache due to heat. To extract foreign matter from the eye, a bean is inserted; and to remove afterbirth, the mother is given three raw *frijoles* to swallow. It is common knowledge that beans are a cause of flatulency—hence the numerous teas that have been evolved to counteract it.

While visiting a young Indian woman to congratulate her upon the recent birth of a son, I noticed that she had three *frijoles* on her temples. After a little probing, I discovered that this was a Mexican custom, and that it was for headache. "But", I inquired, "how are the beans stuck to the skin?" "Oh", was the response, "if they stick to the head by themselves, it is a sign of illness, but if they do not, it is an indication that the malady has gone, and that they are no longer necessary".

89

FRIJOLILLO

RATTLEWEED   Oxytropis lambertii Pursh
CRAZY WEED
LOCO WEED
PEA FAMILY   Leguminosæ

Even as people often give their friends nicknames because of some outstanding peculiarity or characteristic, they also denote the plants with whom they live by local names descriptive of their habits or appearance or effect. And this is the case with the *frijolillo,* or little bean, so-called after the beanlike seeds this herb produces. Its fruit is contained in swollen pods that allow the seeds to rattle against their interiors when they are shaken by even the slightest breezes, with the result that some English-speaking people have called it rattleweed. Their appelation of crazy weed obviously is a direct translation of the Spanish word *loco,* meaning crazy, and is most suitably applied since stock that consume it when it grows in seliniferous soil develops glassy eyes, a slow and staggering gait and a generally unkempt appearance as if they had gone mad. Gradual emaciation sets in and the animal degenerates until it dies. It is said that stock familiar with the regions where it thrives will not touch it, but that imported animals are unsuspectingly drawn to its inviting leaves and flowers for forage, and that when once tasted it produces an insatiable desire for more. I am told that the antidote against its deadly poison is hot lard (see also *Calabazilla),* and if the afflicted ones can be moved into an uncontaminated region quickly enough, they may recover, especially with constant feeding of grain. However, the increasing paralysis it produces evidently causes abortion and sterility among the animals that have survived in spite of its toxins. It is also believed that when the flowering season is over, the plant is harmless and has no detrimental effects on the cattle and horses that eat it then.

90

GARBANCILLO

PATITA DE LA PALOMA   Lupinus aduncus Greene
LUPINE
QUAKER BONNETS
PEA FAMILY   Leguminosæ

In general, the Spanish New Mexicans have selected this lupine's pea-like appearance for identifying it as *garbancillo*, little pea, but the inhabitants of Cañada de los Alamos evidently feel differently about the matter for they call it *patita de la paloma*, because the leaves resemble a wild dove's claws. Perhaps if they had ever seen a Quaker bonnet, they might also have been struck by the similarity of its blossoms with these charming caps.

According to Charles Darwin ("Movements of Plants", p. 340), the leaves of the lupine are remarkable for "sleeping" in three different ways: from being in the form of a horizontal star by day, the leaflets either fall and form a hollow cone with their bases upwards, or rise, and the cone is inverted, or the shorter leaflets fall and the longer rise; the object in every case is to protect their surfaces from radiation and wetting with dew.

For nearly twenty centuries the word lupine has preserved its Latin designation, *Lupinus*, without any modification, excepting the abandonment in English of the last syllable. There is the legend that Plutarch lived upon lupine, undoubtedly the variety Lupinus albus, and for many years Roman actors paid their imaginary debts upon the stage in lupine seeds, for their round and flat shape mimicked true coins.

The Romans too, introduced lupine into Great Britain, and I found it included in a composite remedy from the Leech Book of Bald, the earliest medicinal Anglo-Saxon manuscript in our possession; so that even had the Romans failed to import it into England, it must have been there from very early times. These are the directions given by the manuscript: "A light drink for the wood-heart; lupin, bishopwort, enchanter's nightshade, helenium, cropleek, hindheel. Take these worts when

91

day and night divide; sing first in church a litany and a credo, and a paternoster; with the song go to the worts, go thrice around them before thou touch them, and go again to church, sing twelve masses over the worts". Furthermore, "The Historie of Plantes", our sixteenth-century friend, tell us that during those days, "the flower or meale of Lupine, with vinegar or boyled in vinegar, swayeth the payne of the Sciatica, it digesteth, consumeth, dissolveth the kings evil, or swelling in the throat, it openeth and bursteth wennes, botches, boyles and pestilential or plague sores".'

Perhaps it was from the Mediterranean that the people of Prado, New Mexico, inherited their cure for running sores on children's faces. The diseased parts are bathed with a tea made from the leaves, and this is followed by an application of the pulverized, dry leaves. When this has been done, a dose of castor oil is administered.

In certain districts, the Astragalus diphysus Gray, a kind of loco weed, is called *garbancillo,* and although the lupine does contain some poison and belongs to the same family as the loco weeds, it should not be confused on this account with the other species which is an entirely different plant.

GERANIO

GERANIUM　　　　　　　　　　　Pelargonium graveoleus L' Her.
CRANESBILL FAMILY　　　　　　Geraniaceæ

Several varieties of geraniums are grown commercially in Europe for the aromatic oil distilled from the leaves as the oil of geranium often replaces attar of roses in perfumes and soaps, and lends its incense to ointments and tooth cleansers.

But *geranio* in New Mexico is the familiar, fragrant-leaved geranium that brightens so many window sills which might otherwise stare at passersby with vacant eyes. The people pot their cuttings in tin cans that once contained peaches, tomatoes, apples, and the like, and they carefully preserve the paper labels so that the effect of the flowers is greatly increased through repetition of colors. Spanish New Mexicans are far more successful than the American residents in having fine large blossoms throughout the winter, and this is doubtless due to the "mold" they gather beneath *piñon* trees, and mix with earth for their tins. An interesting feature of these New Mexican window-gardens is that, handsome as they are, they represent no original outlay of money. All up and down the Río Grande, cuttings and roots of innumerable precious plants, particularly the geranium, are freely exchanged among the housewives, the *Americanos* also joining in this endearing custom, so that there is no house so poor that it is not liberally supplied with brilliant, abundant bloom.

The ready adaptability of the Spanish-Americans here was apparently equal to the utilization of the *geranio* when it was introduced, for they now mash its leaves, add vinegar and salt, and bind the mixture on the forehead as a remedy for headache. And for earache, the leaves are warmed and placed in the ear.

The common rose geranium, which they use in the same way for earache, and which they call *perfume,* may have been given both its English and Spanish names because its leaves smell of roses and a dash of spice if they are touched or bruised; and when cooked, they impart a flavor of roses to the food with which they are mixed.

GUACO

STINK WEED
ROCKY MOUNTAIN BEE PLANT
CAPER FAMILY

Cleome serrulata Pursh

Capparidaceæ

The familiar *guaco* that fringes so many roadsides with its white and orchid pattern, contains a large supply of nectar—hence its name of bee plant.

Iron always has been a favorite medicine for anæmia; and locally, a piece of rusty iron is boiled in water with the flowers. The decoction is strained, and the dose is one glassful drunk cold.

The people of Agua Fría have a somewhat different remedy for stomach difficulties: the leaves are plucked very cautiously, care being taken not to crush them. They are boiled in just enough water so as not to be too dry. A handful of corn and three cloves are put in a bag and boiled with the above preparation for three hours, when the sack is removed. The corn takes away the bitter taste, and the leaves can be eaten as greens with remedial results. And for *torsón en las tripas* (gripes in the intestines), another method is employed: one part of *guaco* leaves is added to one part of *añil del muerto* (goldweed), and both are mashed together and mixed with hot water. The resultant liquid is strained, and the decoction drunk.

I was informed at Ciruela that if the leaves are crushed and placed on the swellings, they will reduce inflammation caused by the bites of all poisonous insects.

But to the Spanish-Americans, the stinkweed, as the bee plant is very commonly called because of the skunk-like odor it exudes, aside from its usefulness in stomach complaints and insect bites, has, in history, served its greatest purpose. A generation ago, the native New Mexican would under no circumstances destroy the weed—remembering well the story of the great drought in which his ancestors would have starved had they not resorted to *tortillas* made from the ground seeds of this plant. Although far from palatable, these seeds are nourishing, and they saved a great many lives during the distress.

The Tewa, Zuñi and San Ildefonso Pueblo Indians have all found that they can make a black pottery paint from *guaco*. Although the coloration is obtained by extensive boiling, the Zuñi, in contradistinction to the Tewa who use the entire herb, do not decoct the root as well. *Guaco* paint produces the dull designs on polished ware from San Ildefonso.

Flies evidently are particularly attracted to this plant while it is still moist, and consequently, great care is taken to prevent their walking on the earthenware while it is being decorated.

This thick fluid may be dried in the sun and kept for an indefinite period. After soaking some of it in hot water, Tewa Indians fry it with grease as a great table delicacy. *Guaco* greens as well may be dried for winter storage if gathered in early summer before the stalks have grown more than about eight inches. These are to be stripped and the slender leaves left in the sun. This method is common particularly among the Keres people. During the process of cooking, the water must be changed several times; and when served, the dish is to be preferred to canned spinach. The Zuñi Indians also cook the tender leaves, usually with corn, and eat them with a generous amount of *chile*.

HABAS

HORSE BEANS
ENGLISH BROAD BEANS
PEA FAMILY

Vicia faba L.

Leguminosæ

During the autumn, when these familiar white beans are gathered here, after having been pulled up by the roots, and stacked in the fields to dry, they are spread over the large, carefully-cleaned, circular, out-door threshing floors. A herd of goats or a group of horses is then driven over the heaped stalks for several hours, to extract the *habas*. The beans are carefully collected, and the remaining chaff is kept to feed stock.

These beans are more nutritious than wheat, and are consequently widely cultivated as a basic food for men and animals. But they also serve other functions in New Mexico. In order to prevent pneumonia or counteract "cold on the lungs", the *habas* are browned in the oven and then boiled. A little salt is added and the soup drunk. But in case pneumonia has already developed, a paste is made from the ground beans and hot water. This is applied, three times a day, to the chest and back, and bound on with a cloth until the pain is relieved.

Another method is to rub the back with oil, "Volcanico", and then sprinkle it with fine powdered *habas*. A soup made with the bean flower often is given to accompany the latter treatment.

A very loquacious *señor* in Cuyamungué told me that ground *habas* were good for *juegos en la boca,* sores in the mouth.

HEDIONDILLA

GOBERNADORA   Covillea glutinosa (Engelm.) Rydb.
CREOSOTE BUSH   or Larrea glutinosa Engelm.
GREASEWOOD
CALTROP FAMILY   Zygophyllaceæ

The creosote bush is a most prudent plant—it practices birth control. It sows the ground about its base with a profusion of seeds, but few of them germinate, for it puts a poison on the seeds which retards their development. And when the poison wears off, most seeds are prevented from germinating by a similar poison carried in the falling leaves. Perhaps this is the creosote bush's method of keeping down the population, especially near its own roots, in a land where there is not sufficient water for closely-associated plant colonies.

The separate bushes grow at a respectful distance from one another, and spread the most arid wastes and the alluvial fans of cañon washes with their warm olive evergreen foliage. At times they fill the surrounding air with a pungent salty aroma, which has given rise to its English name of creosote bush, and its Spanish name of *hediondilla,* "the little bad smeller". It is sometimes called *gobernadora,* "the governess", perhaps because of its supposed regulating effect upon rheumatism, kidney trouble, sores, and wounds.

The people of Tularosa rub the dry and ground leaves upon rheumatic limbs, or boil the leaves in water and bathe with the decoction. They also sprinkle the inside of shoes with the powdered leaves to guard against rheumatism in the feet.

The remedy against kidney trouble is a decoction of the dry or green leaves, taken with a little sugar.

The leaf nodes of covillea are swollen into small warty prominences which are especially resinous, and which doubtless are responsible for the universal belief among both the White and Red inhabitants of the desert that the leaves and twigs, steeped in boiling water and applied to bruises and wounds as a poultice, are especially effective.

An additional characteristic possessed by this bush is that it exudes a thick gummy substance, equal in nearly all respects to the commercial East Indian shellac. This is the result of the work of a scale insect, included in the genus *Coccus,* which punctures the young twigs, lays its eggs in them, and at the same time causes them to exude the gum. Mary Austin and Dr. Edward Palmer say that the Indians used this as a cement to mend broken pottery, make their grass baskets watertight, and affix arrow heads.

Carl Lumholtz, in his valuable book, "New Trails in Mexico", while describing his experiences near the two cone-shaped peaks, Los Picos del Pinacate, recorded this charming tale of Papagoan mythology: "The locality is famous in the legends of the Papago as being the mountain where Iitoi, or Elder Brother, landed after the deluge. He knew, so tradition goes, that the world was going to be flooded, and he saved himself in a cask made from greasewood 'gum' with a cover of the same material. He also taught the coyote how to save himself in a reed. He advised the *pinacate* (see *dormilón*) to go down into the ground, and the vulture to rise high up in the sky. Elder Brother saw how water came forth from the tops of the mountains, and when it was rising he entered his cask which floated four times around the world, and then he landed at Pinacate and was very thin after the long voyage".

Other Indian tribes have found the creosote bush valuable, for the Yavapai at McDowell, Arizona, steam lying-in women four days after childbirth with the leaves and twigs, and drink a decoction of the leaves as a remedy against internal chill.

The Pima Indians chewed and swallowed the gum as an anti-dysenteric; the Maricopa took a weak decoction of its bark for intestinal troubles; and the Apache used its tops as a poultice for rheumatism.

HIGOS

FIGS
MULBERRY FAMILY

Ficus Carica L.
Moraceæ

Nearly everyone knows that the fig has laxative properties, but besides this, the Spanish New Mexicans have found its leaves good for asthma. They are dried and put in a pipe and smoked vigorously. Each draft must be deeply inhaled for then "relief will surely come". At Galisteo, in the event that the navel is ruptured after birth, a fig is cut open and applied.

Hoping to discover some similarity between its New Mexican and Moroccan uses, I carefully investigated the various fig remedies there; and found that the dried fruit is cooked and taken every morning with olive oil for hemorrhoids, and that a liquor is made by distilling the fermented fruit, but I could not discover anyone who smoked the leaves for asthma. They also told me that the ashes of eucalyptus roots mixed with the milk of the fig tree made a good cure for warts.

Our old friend Dodœns, in the "Historie of Plants", has revealed a similar employment in the British Isles during the sixteenth century. "The milkie iuyce of figges", he writes, "is good against all roughnesse of the skinne, spreading sores, tetters, small pockes wheales, or Mesels, freckles, and other such like spottes, both of the body and face, layde to with barley meale parched; also it taketh away wartes, if it be layde to with fatte or grease".

"Figges pounde with Salt Rue, and Nuttes, withstandeth all poyson and corruption. And this was a secret preparation with Mithridates king of Pontus, used against all venome and poyson".

98

HINOJO

SWEET ANISE   Fœniculum vulgare Hill
LADY'S CHEWING TOBACCO
FENNEL
PARSLEY FAMILY   Umbelliferæ

Hinojos
Para los ojos
Son buenos
Para sacarlos

"*Hinojos* are good for the eyes—if you want to pull them out!"

Fennel is a well-traveled plant, and deeply interested mentors upon its introduction to a new society and habitat, as its present wide distribution easily demonstrates. Evidently it first attracted attention for its mustard-colored flowers and its sweet-smelling seeds, in the Mediterranean region. Its spread through present Europe was undertaken largely by Roman hands: it reached England that way, and from there doubtless came over to the Atlantic seaboard of the United States. Doubtless the Franciscan brothers also brought it from México into our Southwest when that region was under Spanish control.

As early as Parkinson's day in England, the fennel seeds were a garnish to fish. They were a flavor to the famous Polish soup, bortsch, and to liqueurs such as anisette of Strasbourg. Culpeper says that its action is carminiative and that it stimulates the secretion of sweat. An oil distilled from the leaves was applied externally in eye lotions (which may have given rise to the verse I have quoted), and internally to correct the taste of unpleasant remedies.

One of the old Welsh physicians of Myddrai said, "He who sees fennel and gathers it not, is not a man, but a devil!", and evidently the Spanish New Mexicans hold this same opinion. They believe that if you boil the fennel seeds in water, adding if you can a little *oro colador* (gold leaf) to the liquid, and drink it in small glassfuls three times a day, that you will be cured of heart trouble. To clear the system immediately after childbirth, the patient is given its seeds to chew, or a tea is administered that has been made by boiling the dry plant. Their directions say that for female trouble, especially for young girls who suffer from a lapse of catamenia, the leaves are chewed and swallowed.

Certain of the Spanish-speaking inhabitants of the state call dill *hinojo,* but this is a misnomer, for *eneldo* and *guijones* are the real Spanish names for dill. Perhaps this confusion may arise because the dill is a member of the fennel family, being Anethum graveolus L. It is used here for flavoring pickled string beans, cabbage, and cucumbers.

HONGOS

MUSHROOMS   Agaricus, Coprinus, Lycoperdon, etc.
PUFFBALLS   Agaricaceæ, Lycoperdaceæ

The Spanish Americans employ the word *hongos* rather loosely, and use it to distinguish any variety of fungus or any growth of a mushroom appearance.

The varieties commonly known as puff balls are powdered, and are placed, with a little cotton, in the ear for broken ear drums; and, to stop flowing of blood from a wound, the dry powder of the puff ball is sprinkled on the ruptured skin. Children sometimes gather these growths to play make-believe volcanoes with them, which they can readily do by merely squeezing the outsides until puffs of smoke arise from the "crater".

There is another kind of fungus, Corn Smut (Ustilago zeæ), that is called *chapetes,* and which grows on corn stalks. Its black powder is mixed with water and spread on the outside of the throat for soreness.

100

HORMIGAS COLORADAS

LARGE RED ANTS

Parents who are anxious about their puny children need worry no more after reading the valuable prescription that I acquired in the following manner: After a couple of hours' interview with an old *médica* in the Sangre de Cristo mountains, I was saying *adíos,* when I noticed a large hill of red ants. I called her attention to the danger of these fiery little insects so near her house. "But no", she said, "it is a great convenience. When a child who is unable to walk is brought to me, I collect a can full of live ants, roast them in the oven, grind them, and rub the child's legs with the powder. After several such treatments, the little one is so strong that he can run and play as well as his companions".

Should one suffer from kidney pains, roasted red ants bound on the back over the pain are said to be most effective. For bedbugs, the beds and bedding are placed on a red ant hill, that the ants may eat the vermin.

In old California, the use of ants in the curing of disease was in great favor. Cephas L. Bard, in an absorbing article entitled "Medicine and Surgery Among The First Californians", appearing in "Touring Topics", January, 1930, mentions the following remedies: "By tapping on an old log—the home of the red ants—they were driven out and collected in a cloth arranged for that purpose. For dysentery they were administered internally as an infusion, the insects being alive when swallowed. Externally, they were applied for the same disease to the bare abdomen, and aroused to anger, so they would bite more freely. The application was intensely painful, but said to be very effectual. In the treatment of rheumatism, the patient was stripped to the skin, placed upon an ant hill, and confined there until he was thoroughly bitten. The soil surrounding the ant hills, mixed with water, was given internally for the cure of diarrhœa and dysentery".

At the pueblo of Ácoma, for stomach trouble the live ants

are entangled in balls of down and swallowed. Their bites, within the stomach, are said to abolish the malady.

Those who believe that witchcraft died in the United States with the last persecutions at Salem are sadly mistaken. For, in New Mexico, the red ants are used for the cure of one who is bewitched. The insects are washed and toasted in an oven. They are then ground, and a small pinch of the powder is put on several pieces of paper, say five or ten. If the supply does not come out even the first time, it is distributed among the papers again. Some water is heated and a teaspoon of "Wizzard oil" and a teaspoonful of sugar are added. One portion of the ant powder is mixed with the liquid for each At the same time, the medals of San Ignacio, San Benito, and L'Escapulario de Señor Carmel are to be worn around the neck.

I am also told that there is a stone, called *arra consagrada,* on the altar of the Cathedral in Santa Fé, which is used by the priest in saying mass. If you can scrape a little from the edge, add it to the drink. "It is better that way, but the priest will not sell the bits of stone, *y es dificultoso encontrarlas*".

HORMIGAS MELIFERAS

HORMIGAS MIELERAS
HORMIGAS MOCHILERAS
HONEY ANTS

The honey ants, or pouched ants, are known for the storage of honey in their abdomens, collected as it oozes from live galls on scrub oak branches growing near their nests. The insects' bodies are so elastic they often become greatly swollen with the amber liquid and children enjoy pinching them and sucking the sweet. This they do with impunity since these ants cannot bite.

They build their homes underground, with a single entrance and, in New Mexico, the ant honey is collected from the nests and mixed with equal parts of *tequesquite* (a crude sodium bicarbonate as it is found near the springs or lakes). This mixture is rubbed on the children's mouths and on their tongues for canker sores.

HUESO DE ABUELO

Hueso de abuelo, literally "the bone of the ancestor", is a grey bone the size of a man's finger, found in the banks of the dumps of ruined Indian pueblos where arroyos have washed away the surface soil and exposed the remains.

An informant of San Juan Pueblo explained that a small quantity is ground and used with other ingredients for undetermined medicinal purposes.

HUESO DE CEREZA

CHERRY STONE   Prunus cerasus L.
ALMOND FAMILY   Drupaceæ

The people of New Mexico carefully save their cherry pits, for should kidney trouble arise, a tea made with the boiled pits may cure it.

And children, who often pick their cherries from neighbors' trees, divide the pits equally among themselves, dig a small hole, and try to throw as many as possible into it. The one who succeeds in getting the greatest number inside wins.

INMORTAL

ANTELOPE HORNS   Asclepiodora decumbens Nutt.
SPIDER MILKWEED
MILKWEED FAMILY   Asclepiadaceæ

Its long, narrow, rather leathery leaves and stiff purple blossoms are borne upon a dull green stem, and like many mountain dwellers, *inmortal* seldom comes down from the higher altitudes of the sate.

English scientists have identified this flower with the Greek

103

god of medicine, Asklepios [Æsculapius], and Spanish New Mexicans cherish it as an excellent remedy for many different pains of the body. They place a teaspoonful of the powdered root in a glass of cold water, and let it stand for twenty minutes, after which the liquid turns yellow. Then they drink a little at a time before breakfast to reduce fever or to relieve headache and pains in the chest. Or the powder may be rubbed over the heart for tremors. In order to reduce the suffering from "cold in the ribs", spasms in the right side, the *inmortal* root is scraped and mixed with a little water, made into a plaster, and placed on the ribs as a poultice. At the same time, one should mix as much of the powdered root as will stay on the point of a knife, in a glass of water, and drink this, holding the glass with the left hand, "so that the pain will go down". If fever should cause pangs in the back of the neck, the ground root is mixed with water and whisky, and poulticed upon the affected part.

Inmortal also takes its place among the remedies used in the difficulties of childbirth. A little of the finely-ground root is given in half-a-glass of cold water for labor pains, and may also be rubbed on the abdomen. After parturition, the mother drinks a hot decoction made from the powder to facilitate the expulsion of the placenta.

Inmortal tea may be taken every hour or so to cure asthma or shortness of breath, and the ground root is snuffed up the nostrils for catarrh. It acts like snuff and causes violent sneezing which is supposed to banish the malady.

JARITA

SANDBAR WILLOW   Salix exigua Nutt.
WILLOW FAMILY   Salicaceæ

In old Spanish the word was sometimes *xara,* meaning shaft, from Arabic *xara,* meaning branch *(mata),* coming in turn from the Hebrew *khara,* to cast. In New Mexican Spanish it is *jarita.*

104

In a region where toothbrushes are scarce, and the staple diet is beans, meat and chile, it is not surprising that pyorrhœa should be a fairly common disease. The leaves of the *jarita* are chewed to harden the gums in the event this malady arises, and the small branches are chewed, after the bark has been removed, for the same purpose.

The Pima, Apache, Mohave, Winnebago, and Dakota Indians took a decoction of the leaves and bark as a febrifuge.

The bark of the round-leafed variety, called *jara de la hoja redonda* at Truchas, is boiled there as a tea for pyorrhœa, and it also furnishes a dye and a substance that is used in curing hides. The bark is placed in a wooden trough and crushed in water, then the skin to be prepared is soaked in this solution for a week. This method turns the hide dark brown or black. In olden times, goat, dog, and deer hides were cured in this manner and were used for the tops of shoes, cow hides furnishing the leather for the soles. These boots had no heels, and were sewn entirely by hand.

LAMA DEL AGUA

ALGÆ
GREEN ALGÆ FAMILY   Chlorophyceæ

Lama del agua literally means slime of the water, and is a common hair-like green algæ to be found growing in the backwash of New Mexican streams.

One of my generous informants whose gift it was to enliven many pleasant hours with stories of his childhood said that everyone found it excellent for nose-bleed. You must place the fresh moss on the back of the neck, and allow it to remain there until it has turned yellow; then these troublesome afflictions will either cease or at least become infrequent.

LANTÉN

LLANTEN   Plantago major L.
YANTEN
COMMON PLANTAIN
PLANTAIN FAMILY   Plantaginaceæ

This herb was given its Latin name because of the shape
of its leaves, which resemble the sole of a shoe: *planta,* meaning sole and *ago,* meaning like.

Even at the present time, there is a belief which exists in
connection with the plantain. It is said to follow the Englishman, and suddenly appear wherever he may make his home.
There are evidently so many testimonies to give credence to
the story that it is quite generally accepted, and certain Indians
formerly called it "the Englishman's foot".

The New Mexicans of Spanish descent crush its green
leaves, add a little salt, and bind them on the head to secure
relief from headache.

LAUREL

CLEANDER   Nerium Oleander L.
DOGBANE FAMILY   Apocynaceæ

"That is a tree of the Sun, and under the celestial sign
Leo, and resisteth witchcraft very potently, as also all the
evils old Saturn can do the body of man, and they are not a
few; for it is the speech of one, and I am mistaken if it were
not Mizaldus, that neither witch nor devil, thunder nor lightning, will hurt a man where a bay tree is".

This is the manner in which Culpeper prefaces his re-
marks about the laurel of history, Laurus nobilis, under which
the people of Rome were advised to shelter themselves during
the many visitations of plague that threatened the Eternal
City, and whose leaves were woven into garlands, to crown
poets, and hence become associated with a sense of fame and
reward.

106

Laurus does not grow in this region, and it can therefore only be obtained from the pharmacies. Its wide use as a flavoring for foods is well known, and the Spanish-Americans here drink a tea made from the leaves for fevers.

They also give the name of *laurel* to the familiar oleander, which they tend in brilliant paper-covered tins during the winter, and move from broad window ledges inside their houses to the gardens during summer months. Besides being appreciative of its beauty, they consider it valuable in curing headache or neuralgia. They grind the dry leaf and rub it on the brow, or upon the afflicted parts.

LECHE DE BURRO

Goats' milk and asses' milk have long been considered excellent foods and remedies, as anyone will tell you. And recently one proud burro owner explained. "This year the mothers have plenty of milk, and that is good; you know I always carry it to town for the tubercular people to drink. It has saved many lives".

LECHE DE CONEJO
(Rabbits' Milk)

Without wishing to enter into a discussion of the difficulties attending its collection, I have been assured that lice are exterminated by one application of rabbits' milk. But if, by some unfortunate circumstance, one should be prevented from securing this valuable substance, an Indian from Santo Domingo affirms that a Navajo on the Apache reservation told him that just a dab of rabbit's fat on the nape of the neck will banish both lice and nits.

LECHE DE VACA

(Cow's Milk)

For infants' sore eyes, cow milk is diluted with water and dropped into the eyes; but in Syria, the nursing mothers use their own warm milk.

The Spanish New Mexicans also will tell you that if you suspect the presence of an *ajalote,* or a *guajalote* as they are called sometimes, in your house, you must discover this salamander and dispatch him without delay, as he is especially dangerous to women. It is believed that at night the animal will emerge, crawl about and even creep into bed, and if that bed should be occupied by an expectant mother, the creature would contrive to destroy her child. Should the victim of such an invasion realize her predicament in time, she can prevent calamity by quickly sitting over a pail of hot milk into which the *guajalote* is bound to be attracted.

Another informant tells me that at times of great storms, black and yellow ones fall from the sky, and that they will even attack women during the menstrual period and devour the living flesh.

Further investigation has revealed that these beliefs still obtain in California and old México as well.

Doubtless the tiger salamander (Ambystoma tigrinum) is the animal around which these attitudes center. The larvæ, which are green and black, live in water until their gills are absorbed, whereas the adults, being terrestrial, have to live in moist, damp, secluded places where they are rarely seen or collected. But after a rain, they come out of hiding and travel over the ground looking for worms, and other food, which gives rise to the superstition that they fall from the skies.

LECHEROS

MILKWEED   Asclepias speciosa **Torr.**
MILKWEED FAMILY   Asclepiadaceæ

This milkweed grows to a considerable height in comparison with other members of its family, and is something of a traveler, since it has been found from Canada to México.

In Taos, its young leaves or immature pods are cooked like green beans and added to meat dishes, to increase their palatability, or to increase the size of the dish should an unexpected but welcome visitor arrive.

The Tewa women take an infusion of the entire plant for sore breasts, and decoctions of the milkweed are given to the mothers if they have faulty lactation.

LECHONES

MILKWEED   Asclepias galioides **H. B. K.**
MILKWEED FAMILY   Asclepiadaceæ

Different localities have different local names for surrounding plants, and his Asclepias, which usually is called *lechones,* is an excellent example of such differentation. In Galisteo, it is termed *lechugas* and *lengua de vaca,* and, at Cienega, it is referred to as *lechuria.*

If one should suffer from "pains in the face", the milk from this plant should be applied immediately, and "it will draw out the soreness."

The use of this milkweed, which is fed to female cattle, goats and sheep to increase their lactation, is an excellent modern example of the survival of the ancient "doctrine of signatures". This belief was based on the theory that plants and minerals were supposed to be marked by some natural sign or symbol which indicated the particular medicinal use to which they could be put; thus, yellow flowers were to be used for jaundice, and the bloodstone was to be taken as a cure for hemorrhage.

Children delight in stripping off the outside of the green pods of Asclepias galioides and eating the insides, and in the early spring the Zuñi Indian boys search for the plant in order to eat its fresh buds.

"The pods are gathered for spinning when about two-thirds ripe; the Zuñi say that the fully ripe coma cannot be used for this purpose. 'When the plant is gathered at the proper time', they say, and is perfectly fresh, the coma is sufficiently pliable to work; but after the second day following the gathering of the 'cotton', it must be lightly sprinkled with water.

"The aged Zuñi declared at the time of the writer's first visit to the pueblo, in 1879, and they continue to assert, that beautiful white dance-kilts, women's belts, and other articles were woven from the fiber of Asclepias galioides", writes Matilda Cox Stevenson.

Other writers have affirmed that the fibers of this plant have been used by several Indian tribes to make twine and ropes.

LECHONES

MILKWEED
MILKWEED FAMILY

Asclepias latifolia Torr.
Asclepiadaceæ

The Asclepias latifolia, as its name implies has thick, broad, nearly oval dark green leaves which grow quite close to each other on a stout erect stem. When young, the entire plant looks as if it were covered with a fine dusty powder, but it soon loses this characteristic and becomes a smooth green. It produces a clustered inflorescence of a greenish color which later give rise to the well-known silky seed pods of the milkweed.

Its stems are cut into several segments and placed in the sun so that the balls of fluid which appear at their ends may be dried and then used as chewing gum after such exposure. The fresh sap is applied to sores to reduce their irritability, and to warts. This thick liquid also is regarded as a "complexion balm", and is applied wherever any concentrated pigmentation of the skin occurs, as for example, in the case of freckles.

LECHUGUILLA

SAND VERBENA   Abronia fragrans Nutt.
FOUR-O'CLOCK FAMILY   Nyctaginaceæ

This is another plant which the Spanish New Mexicans refer to as *lechuguilla*. It has oval leaves, usually an erect stem, numerous white flowers, and varies between being covered with a dusty white powder and a hairy, somewhat sticky surface.

It is considered an excellent lacteal stimulant: The entire plant is collected in August, washed and dried, broken into pieces, ground, and boiled in water until a syrup is obtained. This then is strained through a cloth. Thereafter, every third morning before breakfast, half-a-cup of the warm liquid is taken. The third or final dose is drunk on the ninth day. Every time the remedy is imbibed, the breasts are bathed with the same preparation.

LECHUGUILLA

INDIAN HEMP   Apocynum cannabinum lividum A. Nels.
DOGBANE
DOGBANE FAMILY   Apocynaceæ

Lechuguilla, to be sure, is an attractive name and a musical one, but, withal, likely to prove misleading, since I found that it was applied to at least two entirely different plants in New Mexico, and that the Spanish Californians call a species of *agave* by the same word.

In the vicinity of Santa Fé, the stems of this dogbane are broken and placed in the sun so that it will dry the milk they release. Then the little desiccated balls are used as chewing gum.

111

LEMITA

THREE LEAF SUMAC   Rhus trilobata Nutt.
SKUNK BUSH
FRAGRANT SUMAC
SQUAW BERRY
SQUAW BUSH
LEMONADE BERRY
SPICE BUSH
CASHEW FAMILY   Anacardiaceæ

The *lemita* is a cousin of poison ivy and poison oak, and sometimes is confused with the latter, although this is entirely unnecessary. To be sure, both plants attain a similar height and are found growing in similar regions, and both have three leaves at the ends of their branches, but there the resemblance ceases. The poison oak produces white berries and the *lemita* grows bright red berries having a pleasantly acid taste, which are coated with a hairy stickyness. The leaves of the *lemita* do not possess the shiny glossiness of the poison oak's, are somewhat smaller, and release a pungent scent when bruised.

With the possible exception of the various willows, squaw bush is the most widely used shrub in the making of Indian baskets. The warp is formed from the peeled branches, and for a weft and sewing material in the weaving of coiled baskets, the branch usually is split into three pieces, the bark and brittle tissue next to the pith are removed, leaving a flat, tough strand. It has been employed in this manner by the Apache, Panamint, Paiute, Navajo, Hopi, and Coahuilla Indians. The latter, who lived in San Diego County, California, gave a deep black color to the strands of the three-leaf sumac by soaking them for about a week in an infusion of the berry stems of elder *(flor de sauz)*. Among the Zuñi Indians, the stems with the bark removed are used in making the fine "Apache" and other baskets, and the bark-covered stems are employed to form the patterns in the weave.

In my early youth at Fort Whipple, Arizona, I saw Apache squaws make bread out of the ground *lemita* berries, and at present the Tewa Indians eat its fruit whole or ground. Since

112

the duty of collecting its stems for basket-making, and its fruit for food, nearly always fell to the squaws, doubtless this accounts for its popular name of squaw bush.

The Spanish-Americans of New Mexico have found that the plant may be beneficial to them. To make the hair grow, after shampooing, they rinse it with a decoction of the roots. The people of Ciruela grind the dry bark into a powder and rub it on a sore mouth. Moreover, they say that the gum from the bush is good to chew.

Many travelers in this region have found relief from thirst by sucking its acid-tasting berries which stimulate the flow of saliva, and many inhabitants make a refreshing beverage from its fruit, particularly welcome during the heat of summer days.

According to Paul Standley, the Navajo made a black dye from a decoction of its leaves and berries when combined with the calcinated gum of the *piñon,* whereas the Spanish-Americans employed the twigs and leaves for the same purpose.

LENGUA DE VACA

YELLOW DOCK
CURLED DOCK
NARROW DOCK
SOUR DOCK
RUMEX
BUCKWHEAT FAMILY

Rumex crispus L.

Polygonaceæ

Although the Polygonaceæ have given us the better known buckwheat and rhubarb, the *lengua de vaca,* cow's tongue (so-called from the shape of its leaves), has some pretentions of its own to a place in the herbal hall of fame.

The yellow dock is distributed widely throughout the state, growing profusely in waste grounds, alfalfa fields, ditch banks, and about rubbish. It produces its pale green clustered flowers in June and July; later they turn to a deep rust red. The root has scarcely any odor, but possesses an astringent taste, perhaps due to the high percentage of tannin it contains.

113

Its leaves, considered excellent as "greens", are mashed, mixed with salt and bound on the forehead for headache, and the roots are chewed to counteract pyorrhea.

According to "Quivira", by Paul A. Jones, many Indian tribes have used its roots for diarrhea.

The Spanish New Mexicans give it the name of cow's tongue, showing a similar thought to that of the Moors, who have called it by the pseudonym of the "tongue of the lamb".

LIMONCILLO

ASTER FAMILY   Pectis angustifolia Torr.
                                      Compositæ

This plant is called *limoncillo,* literally "little lemon", because it exudes a strong lemon-like odor.

The Spanish-Americans make a tea from the entire plant to relieve stomach pains.

LINASA

LINSEED   Linum lewisii Pursh.
WILD FLAX
FLAXSEED
FLAX FAMILY   Linaceæ

Although Linum lewisii Pursh. once grew so plentifully in New Mexico that there was a river named for it, the cultivated seeds for remedial uses now are purchased at the pharmacies.

Nearly everyone's grandmother could have told you that a linseed poultice was good for any kind of inflammation, and the people of Spanish descent here still employ it for that purpose. They also grind the dry seeds, mix one teaspoonful of this powder with two teaspoonsful of corn meal, and add sufficient boiling water to produce a paste. It is bandaged two or three times a day on infected wounds, and applied to reduce swellings and mumps. A similar treatment is given for boils

114

and sore throat, and, if this is not effective, the ground *linasa* alone is mixed with a little water or vinegar and poulticed on the soreness.

LIRIO
IRIS
IRIS FAMILY   Iridaceæ

The Spanish New Mexicans assert that the iris roots are poisonous. Through what evidently is a quirk of terminology, they refer to the plant at *lirio,* whereas the strict Spanish translation of the word is lily and not iris. After considerable searching for the origin of their belief that the roots are poisonous, I found that the Moors, from whom the New Mexican Spanish have derived so much of their herbal knowledge, say that the tubers of the alum lily contain poison. In time of famine or after a drought, however, the Moors boil the bulbs in several waters, and dry and grind them into a meal, of which a sort of cake is baked. They also make improvised plates from the leaves, which are especially useful for stacking cheeses.

Doubtless if one were sufficiently courageous, he could experiment similarly with the iris roots and discover for himself whether boiling in several waters would extract the poison and thereby make them a suitable and nourishing food.

However, New Mexicans believe that smallpox can be treated with the *lirio* roots. These are sliced and threaded on a cord, and the necklace is tied around the throat. They say that smallpox closes the throat, and that the band of *lirio* roots around the neck will open it when this remedy is employed.

That the provocative properties of the roots were well known in sixteenth-century England is evident from this quotation: "The greene and new gathered rootes of Iris, and especially the juyce thereof, doo purge downward mightily, and bring forth yellow choler, and almost al waterish humours, and are therefore good against the dropsie, but they may be

115

taken but in small quantitie, and yet they ought to be well mingled with things that coole, for otherwise they will inflame the very bowils."

MAÍZ

CORN
GRASS FAMILY

Zea Mays L.
Gramineæ

This way from the North
*   Comes the cloud,*
Very blue,
*   And inside the cloud is the blue corn*
How beautiful the cloud
Bringing corn of blue color!

This way from the West
*   Comes the cloud*
Very yellow,
*   And inside the cloud is the yellow corn.*
How beautiful the cloud
Bringing corn of yellow color!

This way from the South
*   Comes the cloud*
Very red,
*   And inside the cloud is the red corn.*
How beautiful the cloud
Bringing corn of red color!

This way from the East
*   Comes the cloud*
Very white,
*   And inside the cloud is the white corn.*
How beautiful the cloud
Bringing corn of white color!

How beautiful the clouds
From the North and the West
From the South and the East
Bringing corn of all colors!

Corn-Grinding Song—Tesuque pueblo. Translated by Natalie Curtiss

Corn and Indians long have been closely-correlated words because they have been consistently associated since the discovery of the New World; and so familiar and characteristic

116

a North American plant needs no introduction to recommend it to the interest of those who read this book.

Scientists believe that corn is autochthonous in the Americas, and among the botanists it is known that a coarse native grass of our Southern States—teosint or teocentle—can be specialized, as proven by Luther Burbank, in sixteen generations, to produce a kind of *maíz;* but there are recognized indications that the grain may have developed in one of the plateau regions far to the south. It is supposed that this development took place through some twenty thousand years, and it is known that all the varieties now in use, such as dent, round- and pointed-grained, and pop corn, were developed before the White man appeared in the New World. And no particularly improved methods of raising it have been added since.

Indians have their own explanations to account for its origin and also for its variously colored strains. The following myth of the Zuñi is only one of many legends on the same subject: Their ancestors selected large and beautifully colored grass seeds, to the number of seven different kinds of seven different shades, these being the yellow, blue, red, white, streaked, black, and all-colored; and ceremonially planted one of each with feathered wands of corresponding hues. The yellow, blue, white and red they planted according to the four world regions, the cardinal points of the compass, but being puzzled about where they should place the other three, they glanced at the sky, for it was night, and saw there the seven great stars. With gladness and rejoicing, they planted the remainder according to the position of the other three stars outside the heavenly square. They were then fertilized by the ritual union of the youth Yá potuluha with the Seven Corn Maidens, beautiful as the seven stars, and the different kinds of corn sprang up according to the colors of the former grass seeds, and thus we have the various corns.

The Río Grande Tewa plant corn in April. As with all other seeds, "it should be sown under a waxing moon, so as to grow with the moon; under a waning moon the seeds cease growing". It is gathered in late September or early October, after the watermelons have been harvested. "The *gobernador* proclaims the day on which people are to begin to take their corn, and at the more conservative pueblos, for instance at Nambé, no one dares to take it before the time". At the time of husking, the best ears are saved for seed, but not all of them are planted the following year, but are kept two winters, for if the first planting should fail, then they would have no seed. A few husks are left on the seed corn, and they are woven together with *ristras,* much like the *chile,* and hung over the parapet of the roof to dry before winter storage.

There is a story that in ancient times women did not have to grind; they simply laid the *mano* and the corn on the *metate* and it ground itself. However, in these parlous days, nothing like that has been known, and the women are forced to pulverize the kernels. Several women grind together at night; on four *metates* ranging from rough to fine. On the first they break up the kernels and on the fourth finally reduce them to a fine powder. Meanwhile the men sing the grinding song or beat upon a drum, and the women keep time with their *manos* in slow regular strokes.

Corn meal has many ritual uses, and a bowl of it is kept in a niche by the door of every house to be sprinkled much in the manner of holy water; white corn meal primarily is a woman's offering, as feathers are the offering of the men. When the impersonators of the katchina visit a house, the women welcome them by throwing corn meal to each in turn. At public dances in the Tewa plazas, several old men pass along the line of dancers, throwing meal to each and uttering requests on behalf of the village. The clowns in the dances also wear meal-bags at times and occasionally sprinkle from them. Upon the naming of a child, the face, breast, and hands are powdered with corn meal, and the walls of the room should be "painted" with meal in four places. Great care is taken by the Zuñi as well as by many other Indian peoples to obtain corn in a variety of colors for ceremonial purposes. They must have the four colors of the cardinal points, as well as black for the nadir and all colors for the zenith.

Naturally, corn is one of the most important of Indian foods, and is made into wafer bread, the *guallabe* of the New Mexican Spanish, the *piki* of the Hopi, the *hewe* of the Zuñi, and the *mowa* of the Río Grande Tewa; and into *atole,* a kind of gruel, and *posole,* a form of hominy. Cooked foods are appropriate gifts and corn in various forms frequently is given to one's neighbor. But however charmingly presented, it is understood that the "gift" will be returned in some other form by the recipient. At different times varying amounts of corn were traded for buffalo hides. At Santa Clara pueblo, corn served as a tally in the election of the governor.

Any substance which is as important as corn from a nutritive and ceremonial point of view, necessarily carries with it some medicinal utility. At San Ildefonso pueblo, corn pollen especially was recommended for palpitation of the heart, and with what seems due regard for the "Doctrine of Signatures", black corn with a slight streaking of red is good for women at their menstrual periods. The Comanche, Kiowa, Blackfeet, Crow, Sioux, and Arapahoe Indians all took the ground meal steeped in lye as an intestinal antispasmodic.

The Maya in their medicinal texts prescribe raw *maíz* soaked in water for blood in the urine; the grain also was roasted and crushed with the *macal-kuch* (Discorea spiculiflora, Hemsl.) to poultice a sore or swelling caused by sorcery.

Curiously enough, I have learned that the dry *espigas de maíz* are considered very effective against witches by the Spanish New Mexicans. They say that this is because the stems of these flower spikes appear to form a cross. In order to cure a sick person suffering from bewitchment, the *espigas* are burnt with a match, a little water is added to the ashes and the patient drinks the substance. But another method to ease the external pain caused by witchery is to light the *espiga*

119

de maíz over a plate, collect the ashes and rub them on the place where the pain is centered.

The Spanish New Mexicans also have developed treatments for many ills through the use of corn in various forms. They make a mush from the blue meal *(chaquegue),* and apply it hourly to bullet wounds until they are healed. The *cabello de maíz* (corn silk) is boiled in water, and taken, with the addition of *piloncillo* (Mexican brown sugar), three times a day as a diuretic. The dry corn is employed as a diaphoretic for pneumonia. It is crushed and sprinkled over a pan of hot coals. The patient is placed on his back with knees up, and without clothes. The pan of coals and corn is placed under the knees and a sheet and blanket complete the covering of the afflicted person. The hot pan must be renewed three times and the patient must be allowed to sweat for three hours. Then a purge is administered of two teaspoons of "saltrastica" in a cup of senna tea.

For those afflicted with asthma, a teaspoon of the *flor de maíz* (corn flower) is boiled in a cup of water and drunk three times a day. A blind woman at Peña Blanca, whose mother was a famous *médica,* gave the following confirmation of its virtues: "My husband suffered from a bad cough for two years and he consulted many doctors but they were unable to help him. Finally, he took this very good remedy and he was soon cured".

Though I have discussed the wide and varied utility of corn in New Mexico, significantly enough, our "Historie of Plantes", published in London in 1578, has very little to say of its virtues. "This grayne groweth in Turkie wher as it is used in the tyme of dearth", it states, and that "there is as yet no experience of the natural virtues of this corne".

MALVA

MALVA DEL CAMPO
MALVA MEXICANA
MALLOW
CHEESES
MALLOW FAMILY

Malva parviflora L.

Malvaceæ

Of the mallows, Pliny said, "Whosoever shall take of the mallows shall be free from all diseases", and the famous Greek physician, Pedacius Dioscorides, who compiled one of the earliest of all herbals, highly praised the mallow for its virtues. He was said to have been the private attendant to Antony and Cleopatra, and was greatly respected as the source of herbal therapy for sixteen centuries.

At various times, the Anglo-Saxons have used *malva* as a food, a cataplasm, and a cathartic; and because of its demulcent properties, as a relaxing poultice in cases of external inflammation.

The Spanish New Mexicans regard *malva* as a remedy for "All the ills that men endure" (Cowley). They boil its leaves and wash with the resultant tea whatever pimples from whatever disease may appear on the body; they take the decoction for fever, and consider it a valuable aid in causing perspiration during sweat baths. Headaches are cured by mashing the leaves, adding salt and vinegar, and by placing the mixture on the temples. They say mallow is an excellent emmenagogue and use it for pneumonia. The powdered dry leaves are blown into the throat and are supposed to relieve swollen glands.

In order to clean out the system after childbirth, the leaves are boiled, the liquid is strained, *piloncillo* (Mexican brown sugar) is added and the infusion drunk. Another more elaborate method is to boil fifteen or twenty-five green leaves, or preferably dry leaves, with one-third cup of raisins, and a cup of water, for an hour. This should be done at night and the preparation placed out-of-doors so that the dew reaches

121

it. In the morning it is eaten by the women the first, second, and third day after childbirth.

The mallow grows where hard-pan and clay suitable for pottery-making exists, so the Indians always look for the mallows as an "indicator" of the position of the material they need for their pottery.

At Santa Clara pueblo, it is used as a remedy for headache. The ground plant is made into a paste with the addition of water and a small quantity of sugar. This is applied over each temporal artery and on the forehead between the eyebrows.

MALVA DE CASTILLA

MALVA ROSA   Malva crispa L.
MALLOW
MALLOW FAMILY   Malvaceæ

This species of mallow is grown in the gardens and is much taller than the *malva mexicana,* but it, too, is of wide utility among the Spanish New Mexicans. For measles and hoarse throat, they drink a hot decoction of its leaves, and poultice them for boils and bruises. The tea made from this *malva,* with the addition of a teaspoonful of salt, is given as an enema to women. And for after-pains of childbirth, half a teaspoon of *tequesquite* (crude sodium bicarbonate as it is found near the springs or lakes), four or five raisins, and a teaspoonful of dry *malva de castilla,* are boiled in half a pint of water; this is then strained and drunk three times a day. These quantities suffice for one dose.

I was glad to find that the Moors have similar uses for the *malva:* they drink its tea for coughs, wash wounds and sore eyes with the decoction; and cook the greens and prepare them with raisins and olive oil because of its laxative properties.

122

MANTECA DE ZORILLO

SKUNK LARD

Rheumatism is a common complaint in New Mexico, and a considerable number of cures make use of the fat of animals for "the thousand natural shocks that flesh is heir to". Among these remedies, *manteca de zorillo* enjoys particular favor. When some one has an attack of rheumatism, a little skunk fat is warmed at night, and brushed on with a turkey feather. Then the tortured limb is bound with flannel.

Mr. Walter R. Smith, the author of a relevant article "Animals and Plants in Oklahoma Folk-Cures", "Folk-say", cites several additional usages of skunk lard in Oklahoma. "Taken internally", he writes, "it is very effective in case of croup. Rubbed on the chest it relieves cold on the lungs or even pneumonia. Insect bites or skin disorders are helped by using skunk grease as an ointment".

MANZANILLA

MANZANILLA DE ALEMANIA   Matricaria courrantiana DC.
CAMOMILA
CAMOMILE
SWEET FALSE CHAMOMILE
WILD CHAMOMILE
PINEAPPLEWEED
ASTER FAMILY   Compositæ

The well-known German camomile doubtless is so familiar to everyone that it needs no further descriptive introduction.

If an earache should arise, the dry flowers are warmed, placed on a small piece of cotton, and put in the ear; and for neuralgia, one should take the skin of an onion, warm it, spread it with *manzanilla,* and place it on the afflicted part. Camomile is also considered an excellent rinse for the hair.

The Latin name of *Matricaria* is derived from *matrix,* womb; perhaps because this plant was so highly regarded as a remedy for the difficulties associated with childbirth, and

123

for women's complications; in any event, it is still accorded deep respect for those purposes by the Spanish New Mexicans. A pinch mixed with vaseline is used for young girls with womb trouble; and, in order to produce menstruation, beginning nine days before the time due a teaspoonful of olive oil is added to a cupful of tea made with *manzanilla,* and administered to the patient.

For children with colic or a baby given to vomiting, a tea made with *yerbabuena* (spearmint), *manzanilla,* and *alhucema* (lavender) is a favorite recipe.

After childbirth, the mother takes *manzanilla* tea until she is well-cleansed.

La mollera (the fontanel or soft spot on a baby's head) which is believed to cave in and cause illness, is treated as follows: The midwife boils a pinch of *manzanilla* in a little water. When it is still lukewarm, she takes a small quantity of the tea in her mouth and then putting her lips to the child's head, sucks until the *mollera* has resumed the correct position. After the sucking, salt may be put on the spot, or, better, a piece of linen is spread with the thoroughly beaten white of an egg, placed on the head, and allowed to dry there. Another method of bringing up the fontanel is to fill a pail half-full of warm water, then, taking the baby by the feet, to dip the top of his head in the water. The suction, as his head is pulled out, raises the fontanel. Then the white of an egg is applied as before. All sorts of ailments are attributed to the falling of the soft spot, but these methods "will surely cure it".

Manzanilla, which literally means little apple, also is employed as a remedy against *purgación* (gonorrhea). Half of a medium-sized onion is soaked overnight with a sprinkling of powdered *manzanilla* flowers in a cup of cold water. To this, a teaspoonful of sugar is added the following morning, and the entire cupful is drunk early every morning for five days, and thereafter every other morning until the ninth. For breakfast, follow this with *cota* tea (see *Cota* **P.**) instead of coffee, but after the ninth morning when the onion and

124

*cot*a treatment is discontinued, *canutillo del llano* tea (Mormon tea) should be taken with a little brown sugar, one cup at a time, three times a day until a complete cure has been effected.

In the bustling days of old California, *manzanilla* tea was given as a diaphoretic; at present, in New Mexico, it is drunk for stomach trouble and fever.

There are several parallels between the present *manzanilla* remedies in New Mexico and in Morocco. The Moors now boil the plant for tea and this is good for colds, bronchitis, for purifying the blood and "is very good for the abdomen". If the boiling process is performed in a new earthenware jar, the decoction is considered excellent for sore eyes.

MARAVILLA

WILD FOUR-O'CLOCK   Quamoclidion multiflorum Torr.
MARVEL OF PERÚ
FOUR-O'CLOCK FAMILY   Nyctaginaceæ

The Spanish New Mexicans have evidently inherited the old Latin name for this plant, which used to be *mirabilis,* wonderful. *Maravilla* also means marvel, and the flowers in their blooming are deserving of the old saying: *hacer una cosa a las mil maravillas,* to do something superlatively well.

It is a low, stout, spreading perennial, with heart-shaped bluish-green leaves, and round stems that often are hairy and sticky. This foliage is in strong contrast with its flowers which vary from a gaudy pink to a rich magenta, and have the shape of morning-glories.

The Zuñi men gather its roots and give them to the women of the family who powder and administer them, in cold or warm water, to adults and particularly to children, for relief from the effects of over-eating. The woman puts the medicine into her mouth, ejects it into her hands, and rubs it over the abdomen of the patient. A pinch of the powdered root often is slipped into the water that the young men are to drink at meal-times to prevent their overindulging their appetites.

Tewa Indians drink an infusion of the ground roots for cases of swelling—perhaps those of a dropsical nature.

The merits of the *maravilla* are not restricted to the profusion of its flowers, but extend to its many medicinal virtues. The Spanish *medicas* believe in the efficacy, for dropsy, of the dry roots which may be ground and rubbed on the body, or the same powder, mixed with *punche* (local tobacco), may be applied in conjunction with the following preparation: the flowers of *pónil* (Apache plume) are boiled and mixed with *nistamal* (blue corn meal that has been boiled in lime): this the patient drinks while staying in bed so that violent sweating will ensue.

The people of Prado say that it is good for goiter. First the neck is rubbed with *Volcanico* (a commercial linament) and to this is added the pulverized *maravilla* root from which the outer skin was carefully removed before grinding. A little wool is put in the ears to complete the treatment. An explanation of this final touch was given by an old woman who believed that the air came out of the goiter through the ears and thus reduced the growth. If the disease be of two or more years standing, it cannot be cured as the "blood and poison will go down into the system and cause death".

Should a common sore throat arise, the dry roots are scraped, and the powder is put into a cigarette paper and blown into the throat, but if the complaint proves to be the forerunner of a cold, a hot bath made from a decoction of the roots may be beneficial. Fever can be reduced by mixing the powdered leaves with white vaseline, and by rubbing the whole body with the substance. Mumps can be treated three times a day with an ointment of lard combined with the crushed roots. Finally, camphorated oil should be applied to rheumatic parts and powdered *maravilla* roots bound on with flannel to effect a rapid cure.

MARIHUANA

MARIGUANA   Cannabis sativa L.
HEMP FAMILY   Cannabinaceæ

The leaves of this member of the hemp family act as a counterirritant when ground and rubbed on the body, and the Spanish New Mexicans consequently use them as a remedy against rheumatism.

But *marihuana* also possesses strong narcotic properties, and when it is smoked it produces beautiful dreams, which, however pleasant during their ascendency, are very bad for the nervous system. The smokers of *marihuana* are being placed in the same classification before the law as those who take opium, morphine, or hashish, and the local police are making every effort to stop its growth and sale. Not long ago, an article appeared in a Santa Fé newspaper with the following headline: "Posse Raids Marihuana Patches", and underneath was this sad story:

"The officers found a dozen or more stalks in the center of a flower bed at Baca's place—enough, when it matured, to fill a dozen Prince Albert tobacco tins. The drug is said to sell at five dollars a tin, wholesale, or one dollar a cigarette, retail. They pulled up the plants and brought them to Santa Fé.

"Baca had a ready explanation:

" 'You know these women', said he. 'They always want flowers—and there you are'.

"He didn't know it was *marihuana,* said he, *Por Dios,* no. He was entirely innocent. He had bought a package of flower seeds, mixed, paying fourteen cents for them. Was he to blame if some of these seeds turned out to be *marihuana,* if the officers knew *marihuana* when they saw it?"

127

MARIOLA

SAGE BRUSH   Artemisia rhizomata A. Nels.
WORMWOOD
ASTER FAMILY   Compositæ

This artemisia has multi-branched stems which are covered with white, matted, wooly hairs, as are the oblong leaves.

The New Mexican Spanish chew its fresh or dry leaves for stomach pains, and make a tea of one cup of boiling water and one teaspoonful of fresh or dry *mariola* leaves for rheumatism and stomach ache.

The leaves are powdered and given to expectant mothers with a little water, and the same dose is administered to expel the afterbirth.

MARIQUILLA

GOLDENROD   Solidago canadensis L. Sp. Pl.
ASTER FAMILY   Compositæ

This is a species of the familiar goldenrod that heralds the coming of autumn with its feathery plumes of bright yellow flowers springing from a wand-like stem.

The Spanish New Mexicans mash the fresh plant, mix it with soap, and bind it into a sore throat, and the Zuñi Indians chew it for the same purpose.

Like the sunflower, it makes a light yellow dye, but it has been repeatedly affirmed that no native vegetable yellow has ever been found in New Mexico that is not fugitive, though with the proper choice of mordant, permanency may be achieved, especially with the flower-heads of *chamiso blanco* (Chrysothamnus graveolens Nutt.).

128

MARRUBIO

MASTRÁNZO   Marrubium vulgare L.
MASTRÁNZO MEXICANO
  (Cerro Gordo)
MASTRÁNZO CIMARRON
MASTRANTO
HOREHOUND
HOARHOUND
MINT FAMILY   Labiatæ

Both Hippocrates and Pliny knew the horehound, and an early reference to the plant occurs in one of the twenty-three little poems by Walafred Strabo of Suabia (807-849 A. D.), describing the herbs that grew in the cloister garden at Reichnau, where he was abbot. Oil of roses and horehound tea were his two favorite remedies—the first for outward application, and the other for all internal afflictions.

The present English name is of Anglo-Saxon origin, their word being *harhune, har* meaning gray, and *hun* the name of a plant; but the current Spanish term of *marrubio* is derived from a Hebrew root, *marrob,* meaning bitter juice.

The branches and stems of the horehound are square and covered with a white hairy felt, which together with its rough, blunt-toothed opposite leaves having crinkled margins, give it a hoary appearance, for which it probably received its popular English name. The flowers are quite small cream-colored whorls at the leaf axils, and the leaves themselves have an aromatic odor, but the roots exude a persistent bitter acid taste if put in the mouth.

This plant, which has long been famous in the treatment of colds, was introduced to the Atlantic coast from Europe, and has now spread throughout the United States, supplemented by the early specimens brought to the Southwest by the Franciscan missionaries.

According to the Spanish New Mexicans, one should prepare a hot foot-bath of boiled leaves for chilblains, frozen feet, and rheumatism. The powder resulting from grinding the dry leaves, alone or with lard, is applied to sores of all kinds,

129

and although it may prove very painful, its action is most effective. A mush made from horehound tea and starch is said to relieve stomachache and colic.

Two methods of preparing a remedy against coughs are employed: one is to boil two tablespoonsful of leaves in a quart of water, add one tablespoonful of honey to a cup of hot water, and drink the entire mixture at bed-time. The other consists in boiling together a handful of the leaves and some brown sugar until a syrup is formed. This is strained and a large spoonful of the liquid is given when a coughing fit is precipitated. The above remedy is also supposed to be good for fever and pneumonia.

Another region of the world where similar cures are taken is in Morocco. The Moors drink horehound tea for consumption and coughs, and apply the powdered plant to wounds. They also use it as an ingredient for one of their very elaborate hair dyes that so often make up for what nature may have neglected in personal adornment.

MATA

THOROUGHWORT   Eupatorium arizonicum A. Gray
EUPATORIUM
ASTER FAMILY   Compositæ

The name of Eupatorium was given to a group of the aster family in honor of Mithradates Eupator, King of Pontus, born circa 132 B. C.

Mata is a first cousin of boneset and agrimony, long famous as a diaphoretic, and has leafy stems covered with a fine down, opposite leaves, and white blossoms.

The Indians of Zuñi combine these flowers with those of other plants, in the preparation of cakes which they consider excellent for rheumatism and swellings.

The leaves are very fragrant when burnt, and are smoked by the Spanish New Mexicans. But if a pinch of *mata* is mixed with tobacco or *punche* (native tobacco), it is supposed to make the smoker feel intoxicated.

130

MORADILLA

VERBENA

VERVAIN FAMILY

Verbena ambrosiæfolia Rydb.

Verbenaceæ

The *moradilla,* literally little purple one, is a stout herb with bluish purple flowers, whose name of *verbena* comes from the Latin and means a sacred branch.

If a Spanish New Mexican has pains in the back, he makes a plaster of pitch combined with powdered *moradilla* and places it on the affected part of his body. But if he has "nerves" or rheumatism, he prepares a bath with *moradilla* leaves, and drinks a tea similarly made.

Although a number of other diseases have been confused with leprosy, the ground dry leaves are rubbed on spots that are supposedly symptomatic of this diabolical malady.

MOSTACILLA

PEPPERGRASS

PEPPERWEED

MUSTARD FAMILY

Lepidium alyssoides A. Gray

Cruciferæ

The *mostacilla,* or little mustard, derives its botanical name from the Greek *Lepidion,* little scale, from the shape of its seed pods. It has a general yellowish-green appearance, and creamy white flowers.

The people of Tularosa say that if one mashes the plant and mixes it with powdered lime, and then places the preparation in the wounds of animals, "it will kill the worms".

MOSTAZA

MUSTARD

YELLOW FIELD MUSTARD

MUSTARD FAMILY

Brassica campestris L.

Cruciferæ

This is the local yellow mustard of the open fields, with the peppery properties known the world over.

In a New Mexican family, in case rheumatism develops a

bath is prepared with two handsful of the plant in boiling water. But in the event that a cold begins in the ribs or shoulder of the left side, it should be bound with a plaster made of ground mustard mixed with flour and a little water. In conjunction with this remedy a purge is taken and a warm brick is placed at the patient's feet.

The prepared mustard which can be purchased at food stores is said to be good for paralysis. A large spoonful of it should be put in boiling water to make a bath, and the patient should bathe in it when the liquid has cooled. Another method is to mix a small spoonful of mustard with a plateful of flour and add a small quantity of water. This preparation is sufficient for three or four plasters, one of which should be spread on a linen cloth and bound to the afflicted part each day.

MUSGO

The *musgo* is the common and familiar green moss that grows along the banks of New Mexican streams and brooks.

It is rubbed on sores that are produced by leprosy or some other disease which might have similar symptoms.

NOGAL

WALNUT   Juglans Sp.
WALNUT FAMILY   Juglandaceæ

There is an old adage that *el nogál y el villáno, a pálos hácen el mandádo,* of which the English version is: "A woman, a clown and a walnut tree, the more you beat 'em, the better they be".

The Spanish word *nogal* has been derived from the Latin *nux,* or *nucals,* nut, but the English word walnut is of old Anglo-Saxon origin, having been developed from *wealhhnutu.*

At Córdoba, New Mevico, the inhabitants bathe in a decoction of the walnut bark for rheumatism and for pains in the legs.

132

Elizabethans followed a practice that would be discouraged today, since they maintained that "the new greene Nuttes are much better to be eaten than the dry Nuttes", and their herbalists prescribed a remedy which evidently has been forgotten: "A dried Nut or twayne taken with a figge, and a little Rue, withstandeth all poison".

NOPAL

TUNA
PRICKLY PEAR
BEAVER TAIL
CACTUS FAMILY

Opuntia sp.

Cactaceæ

Have you ever heard of the mythical founding of México City? Nearly any Mexican child can tell it to you. It appears that some five centuries before the arrival of Cortés, the Aztecs came into the region of the present valley of México and were defeated, many being thrust into slavery. But about 1325 the remnants of the Aztecs halted for a brief rest during their painful wanderings, in a marshy spot on the border of a spreading lake. There they saw, on a giant rock that rose above the waters, a *nopal* or tuna cactus, upon which was perched a great eagle holding in his beak a struggling snake. The leaders of the expedition regarded it as a sign of divine wisdom, and believing in omens, immediately began the building of Tenochtitlán—or the place of the tuna—where now stands the present capital of Mexico. This is of interest to New Mexicans because it connects with a local story of about that period, in which all of the forthright young men of the Río Grande pueblos were led away by Poseyemo, one of their outstanding culture heroes, who was directed, by a bird with a snake in its beak, to the land in which they afterward settled. The presumption is that the legend grew out of contact with the Mexican Indians who came north with Coronado in the sixteenth century. Since that time there has been an unconscious effort to consolidate the myths of Poseyemo and the Aztec.

The word *nopal* is simply the Aztec *nocheznopalli* or *nopalli* with the last syllable of the latter lopped off by alien Spanish tongues. The Opuntias to which it is applied have extended from the Atlantic to the Pacific oceans in the United States, and form one of the most characteristic groups of cacti in the landscape of the western hemisphere, where it is native in both continents. There are some thirty species of prickly pear in New Mexico alone, two of the most common being Opuntia Engelmanni and Opuntia Camanchica.

According to Ethel Bailey Higgins, author of "Our Native Cacti", the lobes of the prickly pear are very efficacious for rheumatic inflammations. "The story is vouched for", she writes, "by a mining man of the almost miraculous abatement of inflammation from rheumatism, in the case of a man, brought on a stretcher into Ensenada, Baja California, unable to walk, who in two days was cured as a result of the ministrations of an Indian woman who used cactus lobes". Her treatment consisted in gathering the young joints before they developed spines, then boiling and frying them, and finally applying them to the affected parts.

Moreover, the Spanish Americans of New Mexico will tell you that the *nopal* "leaves", from which the spines have been removed, if roasted and bound while still warm on the side of the neck and below the chin, will reduce the swellings caused by mumps.

Recently, with mingled interest and amusement, I came across the following story of an accidental medical discovery by an old cattleman: " 'Now take tarantulas', he said, 'they're nasty things . . .

" 'Had an experience with one long ago that made me shy of them ever after, I can tell you', he continued. 'I was taking some beeves from the Frio Canyon down to Fort Clark in Kinney County when it happened. We made camp on Turkey Creek . . .

" 'During the night, half asleep, I felt somethin' crawlin' on my face, and in strikin' out to drive it away, I mashed a

134

big tarantula just at the outside corner of my right eye. Didn't think the thing had time to nip me, but his juice ran down my face, and I guess some of it got into my eye.

" 'Well, sir, in the morning, there was a knot as big as a turkey's egg over my right eye, closing it tight. Then I was scared. Told the boys to hold the herd and burnt the earth getting back to Uvalde. Old Doc Cummins lanced the lump, but nothin' come of it. Then he looked serious and said I better lie up and let him treat me.

" 'But those beeves had to be got to Fort Clark on contract time, and I went back to Turkey Creek, with a poultice on to draw out the poison.

" 'The boys had killed a fat brown bear and were feastin' on it when I reached camp. The poultice had grown dry and was hot and stiff, so I took it off and threw it away. Fat bear is greasy meat and after eatin' my fill, I was cleaning my huntin' knife by whacking it into the leaves of a big prickly pear bush near the fire. After cleanin' it, I slashed off a leaf of the plant and split it in two. Just to kill time I tossed the halves of the leaf on the embers of the fire and watched them roast.

" 'The pulp sizzled and steamed and smelled good. It struck me the stuff might make another good poultice; so I scraped it out, plastered it on my neck handkerchief, and bound it over the eye.

" 'Well, sir, that prickly pear done the trick. Next day, the knob over my eye was half gone. Another poultice of the same kind cleaned it out good and the lance cuts healed up quick.

" 'Since then the boys have used prickly pear poultices on themselves and their horses for festerin' wounds from tears of mesquite thorns and nigger heads they get while huntin' beeves in the chaparral' ".

Other old timers will tell you that they often speared *nopal* "leaves", cut them open, and stirred them in muddy water to settle it. This agitation caused the formation of a thick scum on the top of the water, which sank in about half an hour, carrying the sediment with it.

If you were a Southwestern stockman faced with a shortage of forage, you would probably, in the manner of the West, burn off the *nopales* spines, and feed its succulent joints to your cattle. Perhaps it was from this practise that Mr. Burbank conceived the idea of developing a spineless variety.

Early Californians rejoiced in the security of high *nopal* barricades—barricades that were planted rather than built—and found in them, besides, a ready remedy for inflammation.

Those of Spanish descent in New Mexico also cure soreness by burning off the spines, splitting the segments, and placing them while hot on the irritated spots; and use them in the same way for nursing mothers when the breasts become purple from congestion. Swollen glands in the neck are treated with a poultice of *nopal*, ground *toloache* seeds (Datura), and linseed. The *nopal* is first baked in an oven, and the linseed mixed with hot water.

Besides being a remedy for many painful afflictions, the *nopal* has a fruit which can be eaten out of hand or made into sauces and jellies.

If the lobes are peeled, boiled in salt water and fried crisp, they form a delicious dish when served with a sauce.

As I had hoped when I went to Morocco, I found many parallels between Moorish remedies and those of New Mexico. Often plants came into the United States from some part of the Old World, but the prickly pear, contrary to custom, was introduced into North Africa from the Americas. The Moors too, heat one of its flattened joints, split it open and apply it to any swelling on the body, and after the spines are burned off, the plant is fed to animals and is said to increase their milk. Moreover, it is commonly planted to provide quite a formidable rampart about their agrarian villages.

OCOTE
PALO DE OCOTE

TORCH PINE   · Pinus sp.
PITCH PINE
PINE FAMILY   Pinaceæ

We are indebted to the Aztec for the root of the word *ocote,* which was called by them *ocotl.*

The Spanish New Mexicans compound their own "pine cough syrups" by boiling a piece of *ocote* wood in water. Sugar is added to the liquid, and it is administered every morning to those suffering from whooping cough.

Tuberculosis is treated in a similar manner. A very resinous piece of the wood is boiled until the decoction becomes quite thick, and the patient must take a glassful every morning before breakfast.

These remedies are always convenient for the native people who make a practise of keeping chips of this wood on hand for kindling their fires, and in the past they served also as torches when candles were lacking. It is on feast days particularly that *ocote* asserts its importance, as no celebration would be complete without bonfires of pitch pine flaming in the dusk. On such occasions, a man's wealth is shown by the quantity of *ocote* he can display in the number of pyres he builds before his house.

ORÉGANO
ORÉGANO DE LA SIERRA

MONARDA   Monarda menthæfolia Graham
BEE BALM
BERGAMOT
OSWEGO TEA
HAREMINT
HORSEMINT
MINT FAMILY   Labiatæ

This plant is somewhat paler in general appearance than the *orégano del campo,* is perennial, and produces at the ends of its stems purplish flower heads. About the first of October, these form rough globular clusters of calyces containing seeds. It is often brought down from the mountains and placed in the Spanish American gardens where it evidently likes its adopted home and soon spreads as far as its owner and the ever-present weeds will permit.

This monarda also has very fragrant leaves when crushed, and they are used for seasoning many dishes. Roasted kid is sprinkle with *chile* and *orégano* leaves, and they are mixed with frijoles and put into stews to enrich the flavor.

For a cough, the herb is boiled and the tea is drunk while still hot, as often as needed.

At San Ildefonso, the dried plant is ground by the Indians, and its powder is rubbed on the head for headache, or all over the body to reduce fever. At Santa Clara pueblo, it is regarded as one of the "cold" medicines and is therefore used in the treatment of fever, as it is by the San Ildefonso people. For sore throat, a decoction of the leaves is taken internally; at the same time, the Indian patient must put a small quantity of the powder in a deerskin or calico bag, and wear it around his neck.

ORÉGANO DEL CAMPO

HORSEMINT
MINT FAMILY

Monarda pectinata Nutt.
Menthaceæ

This horsemint grows on dry plains, especially in sandy soil, is an annual, and has a rough, sometimes branching stem, and thin leaves very soft to the touch and highly aromatic when crushed. Its flowers are nearly an inch long, and project from crowded heads of purple bracts, while the corolla is a pale pink or lilac.

The New Mexicans of Spanish ancestry use it as a flavoring for many dishes, and as a stomachic.

OSHÁ

CHUCHUPATE (southern New
    Mexico)
PARSLEY FAMILY

Ligusticum porteri C. & R.
Angelica pinnata Wats.
Umbelliferæ

The popular names *chuchupate* and *oshá* are of Indian origin while the Latin name, given by Linnæus, was derived from the Italian province of Liguria.

Oshá, highly-valued mountain herb, occurs as a dwarf and also as a plant of considerable size. The larger plant, which has broad dark leaves variously serrated and wide umbels of yellow terminal flowers, often reaches six feet in height. The smaller kind has white flowers, thinner, paler leaves, much more jagged at the edges, and its growth never exceeds three feet.

Both are highly esteemed, but the sturdier species is considered more powerful medicinally, although prepared in any way, or taken in any manner, the different parts of each have proven a panacea for "all the ills that men endure" (A. Cowley).

There is hardly a native house in New Mexico, be it Indian or Spanish-American, without a small store of the root. It

139

may be chewed for stomach gas or flatulency; it may be ground and taken with water as a stomachic, or cooked, strained, and drunk as a tea. A little of the powder stirred in hot water with sugar and whiskey drives out a cold and a frequent dose will break a chronic cough and benefit flu, pneumonia, and consumption. Even without the whiskey it is helpful, and, taken three times a day, should reduce fever. A syrup made from the stems is equally effectual in all these complaints. The Apaches and, later, the Spanish settlers, smoked the dried hollow stems in place of cigarettes, while the root, on the other hand, is now chewed in an effort to break the tobacco habit. Other Indians, namely those of Cochití, take a piece of root the size of a bean night and morning, and, when it is well masticated with a pinch of salt, wash it down with warm water to shake a cough.

An active life is not unattended by cuts, bruises, and sores, making frequent demands on a supply of some sort of ointment. One excellent recipe for *encerado,* or salve, I learned at Córdoba where yearly rites of the Penitentes increase the need for such a remedy. Some mutton tallow is washed very clean, melted, and strained, a small piece of candle wax and a little *trementina* (turpentine) are added to the hot fat. Powdered *manzanilla* (chamomile), *oshá* root, and that of *contrayerba* (Kallstrœmia brachystylis), complete the ingredients. The proportions are left to individual discretion and the application is made with a clean rag soaked in the mixture and laid over the affliction. If *oshá* root is mixed with olive oil, it is said to form a good liniment for treating rheumatism.

Even the most successful of political tours sometimes are marred by headaches, and this misfortune overtook one of a group of politicians in New Mexico. According to political folklore of the region, an old-timer, of long experience in such matters, reached into his pocket and brought out a section of *oshá* root. He bit off a piece, chewed it well and then spat forcefully on the forehead of the sufferer. In due course, we are assured, a cure resulted.

A paste made of the root powder and a little water is used on snakebites "to draw out the poison". Sheepherders and other campers carry bits of the root in their pockets as a protection against venomous snakes and sprinkle the powder on the ground around their bedrolls to ward off reptiles.

The plant is endowed with a highly pungent odor, which accounts, in some measure, for its alleged effect on serpents, and the scent of its foliage approaches that of its botanical relative, celery. Like those of the latter, *oshá* leaves are used in seasoning soups and other dishes, and may be cooked in a tea for children suffering from colic.

An enterprising pharmacist now is popularizing soothing lozenges, called Martin's Osha (Indian Root) Cough Drops, which contain a percentage of this precious herb.

It is not surprising that a herb of such wide utility should be included in several composite remedies in addition to that for linament. In cases of intestinal stasis, suppositories are made with a mixture of *oshá, añil del muerto* (goldweed), *poléo grande* (Mentha canadensis), a little salt, all moistened and shaped with the aid of a small amount of hot water and *piloncillo* (Mexican brown sugar). When one bolus has been administered, the patient should drink a tea made from *mariola* (sage brush), *añil del muerto* (goldweed), and *chan* (Salvia reflexa, to complete the treatment. In order cases a very effective enema may be prescribed as follows: *oshá, añil del muerto* (goldweed), *poléo grande* (Mentha canadensis), and soap.

PAGUÉ

FETID MARIGOLD   Dysodia papposa (Vent.) Hitchc.
ASTER FAMILY   Compositæ

This plant has received both its English name of fetid marigold, and its botanical name, which is taken from the Greek word *dysodia,* meaning ill-smelling, because its small heads of yellow flowers exude a very strong scent that is somewhat unpleasant.

There is an old saying that "Long as a man can eat, he ain't sick", and the Spanish New Mexicans consider that the use of the *pagué* is one of the best methods of keeping in this enviable condition. They put a bunch of its fresh leaves in a cup and pour boiling water over them, allowing the whole to stand fifteen minutes before it is strained. If the liquid is drunk hot, it will settle your stomach, they affirm; or in even the worst cases of diarrhea and vomiting, the tea will effect a cure *"poco* soon". But if your difficulty should happen to be a stomachache, you should chew the fresh leaves, and if your baby has the colic, you must soak the *pagué* seeds in hot water, and make him drink a glassful of the solution. With these remedies in mind, "there is no reason", they say, "why your family should ever have stomach trouble".

PAJA

STRAW

The generous mounds of glinting straw left from the circular threshing floors of New Mexico have other uses than that of merely feeding stock. It is particularly important in binding the adobe (clay), after the manner of the Biblical injunction of trying to make bricks without straw, and in mixing plaster for the finished house.

These straw mounds also may supply a cure for rheumatism. A large handful of straw is boiled in a tub of water,

142

and three hot stones are added. The patient then puts a board across the tub and sits on it, using a large blanket for covering. This vapor bath must be taken three times a day until the cure is completed.

PALMILLA
AMOLE
PALMILLA ANCHA
PALMA
DÁTIL
YUCA

YUCCA   Yucca baccata Torr.
SOAP ROOT   Yucca glauca Nutt.
SPANISH BAYONET
SPANISH DAGGER
SOAPWEED
ADAM'S NEEDLE
EVE'S THREAD
ADAM'S THREAD AND NEEDLE
OUR LORD'S CANDLES
LILY FAMILY   Liliaceæ

I have always been grateful for the yucca, a plant without parallel in its lonely habitat of rocky slopes or arid plains, seldom blessed with rain, where it blooms in towering shafts of white-flowered beauty. Little wonder that its blossoming stalks have been called Our Lord's Candles, for they stand in a patch of sun like a lighted offering before the storm-darkened skies of summer. The low, bristling clusters of sharp-edged arrowing leaves are truly a forbidding nest for so remarkable an egret of bloom, but they nevertheless serve as a formidable defense for desert survival.

Not all yucca is a dry-country plant. In swampy Louisiana, for example, it frequently grows ten feet high on a sand-

143

bar beside brackish water and may have a stem five inches in diameter.

Before other forms of soap were common in New Mexico, pounded *amole* root was used universally by the inhabitants for all washing purposes, and by the Indians for purification and ritual cleansing as well. After having driven out the Spanish in 1680, they took to the rivers by tribes and shampooed themselves to remove the taint of baptism. With the resettlement, the Spaniards learned to use this root for laundry work, and especially for washing wool; nor has the custom been entirely abandoned since the wide-spread introduction of commercial soap.

The thick yucca roots, particularly of the species baccata and glauca, still are sought after, dug, dried, and stored away. When needed, they are cut or chopped into small pieces, pounded, and soaked in cold water. An excellent lather quickly forms as the roots are stirred and kneaded by hand; the residue is removed, hot water is added to the cold and all is ready. The Indians of Arizona and New Mexico customarily wash their hair with *amole* before all ceremonies, and it may be this "tonic" that gives it such glossy luxuriance. Moreover, woolen blankets seldom are sent to the cleaner's, since the native laundress can make them much more fluffy with *amole*.

Various yuccas long have furnished fibers for many purposes. Archæological remains of the Southwest Basketmaker and Cliffdweller cultures have revealed intricately-woven sandals of this material, as well as ropes, cords, belts, and mats. Even now, cincture pads, baskets, brushes for decorating pottery, whips for initiation ceremonies, brooms, cords for suspending watermelons or similar articles from the ceiling, and for tying bundles of herbs or ceremonial masks, all are made with its many fibers.

Nor is its utility limited to fibers, for American Indians include the fruit, flowers, and *dátil* stalks in their menu. The fruit pods, which vaguely resemble a date in appearance, are

144

boiled or roasted, and yield a very nutritious food, not unlike a sweet potato in flavor. They are also baked as a conserve. After being cooked in this way, the resultant paste is dried and stored away to furnish the future base for a beverage or for a syrup like molasses to be used as a sweetening. Even the flower stalks when full grown, but before the buds expand, are cut into sections, boiled or roasted in the ashes, and eaten after the tough rind has been taken off. The flower buds too, make a palatable vegetable, if boiled; and they serve as a welcome side dish to a diet all too monotonously composed of meat and beans. It is believed at Santa Clara pueblo that the fruit of one kind of *palmilla* is apt to cause diarrhea, and it has also been used to promote easy and complete delivery. At San Ildefonso, it is taken as a ritual emetic, the person first chewing it (probably the root) and then washing it down with water.

An informant in Prado told me that *amole* made a good remedy for *purgación* (gonorrhea). The roots are crushed and boiled in water. One cup of the warm tea is drunk three times a day for perhaps six days, or, she said with great certainty, "until the cure is effected".

Pablo, who sometimes acted as my Jack-of-all-trades, used to amuse me with stories of his childhood in the country, where he had no store-made toys. To replace the daisy chains of children elsewhere, he would string *palmilla* seeds on yucca fiber for necklaces.

On another day, when I was learning the various native ways of making cheese, my elderly teacher casually remarked that *palmilla* was substituted for rennet to curdle milk, "down San Pedro way, but", she added, "I found it really nasty".

It had been intimated to me that some mysterious preparation was used by the secret society of *Los Hermanos Penitentes* as a stimulant. But it was years before I learned, to my surprise, in a whispered conversation, that the same plant that furnishes the material for their scourges also provides the wine taken by the "brothers" before their penance. The *palmillas* (young shoots) are boiled, then mashed, and the juice is poured back into the steaming kettle, the hot water having been retained. It is cooked for an hour or so longer to increase its strength, and a red, wine-like liquid results. This is drunk to make them *"muy bravo y valiente"*. If allowed to simmer several hours more, the wine becomes a syrup that is kept to rub on rheumatic joints.

PALO AMARILLO

FREMONT'S BARBERRY   Mahonia fremontii (Torr.) Fedde
           (Berberis fremontii Torr.)
BARBERRY FAMILY   Berberideæ

Palo amarillo (literally, yellow wood), is a tall shrub which resembles holly, although it has dark blue berries. It grows on rocky slopes such as those between Cerillos and Golden, in New Mexico.

Nearly any older Spanish New Mexican can tell you that the branches and roots are its medicinal parts. The latter are boiled and added to a bath prepared for tubercular patients, who must be treated at least nine or a dozen times before relief may be expected.

The branches may be broken into pieces and also boiled in water for baths to help rheumatism and pains in the ribs. These baths are to be given nocturnally, in sequences of three nights, and a small amount of the liquid should be drunk at the same time. A similar dose is taken for *fiebre amarilla* (jaundice), and since the decoction is a yellow liquid, once again we have a surviving example of the Doctrine of Signatures in New Mexico. Moreover, the *palo amarillo* is a "cold" plant, and should therefore be used in counteracting all kinds of fevers, including malaria.

In the olden days, two small crosses were made from *palo amarillo* wood and attached to the person by leather thongs. One cross was placed on the chest and the other on the back —this would protect the wearer from being struck by lightning.

146

PALO DURO

MOUNTAIN MAHOGANY   Cercocarpus montanus Raf.
HARD TACK
ROSE FAMILY   Rosaceæ

Palo duro, meaning hard wood, was given its Spanish name because of the extreme toughness of the trunks and branches, whereas its botanical name, taken from a combination of two Greek words, *kerkos,* tail, and *karpos,* fruit, was applied because the ripe seeds possess an airy, feathery tail that shimmers in the autumn sunlight and catches the eye with reflected brilliance. Although true mahogany reaches a much greater height, the wood of the *palo duro* has a bright red color when freshly cut, and as it grows on bleak rocky slopes and hillsides, those of English stock have called it mountain mahogany.

At first glance, it seems far-fetched to include this tree in the rose family, but closer acquaintance with its very modest inconspicuous blossoms will convince you that there has been no botanical stretch of the imagination in placing it within that group.

The Spanish New Mexicans hang the leafy mountain mahogany twigs around their beds to keep away bedbugs, or dry them, and put them in little bags which are inserted under mattresses for the same purpose.

The Tewa Indians have found that if they powder the entire young plant by pounding, and stir it in cold water, the liquid forms a good laxative.

On the other hand, the Navajos use it in preparing a reddish dye for their wool. This is produced by mixing a decoction of the mountain mahogany with the powdered bark of the alder (Alnus tenuifolia), and with cedar ashes (Juniperus monosperma). Instead of this concoction, the New Mexican Spanish prefer a mixture of the bark of the tag alder (Alnus icana), with the root bark of mountain mahogany and red ocher, for tinting hides, and making a pigment for their paint.

147

PAPA CIMARRON
PAPAS CIMARRON

WILD POTATO
NIGHTSHADE FAMILY
Solanum Jamesii Torrey
Solanaceæ

Papa cimarron is a perennial that springs from small tubers and is a relative of the potato (Solanum tuberosum). It has small white flowers and pinnate leaves.

This unobtrusive plant is something of a mountaineer, and seldom grows on the lower plains. Therefore the poorer people of the mountain regions eat the tubers for want of potatoes.

PAPAS

POTATOES
NIGHTSHADE FAMILY
Solanum tuberosum L.
Solanaceæ

The early Spanish Californians formerly sliced potatoes and bound them on the temples and forehead for headache, and, at present, Spanish New Mexicans use them for the same purpose. Applications, they affirm, draw out the pain.

PATITA DE LEÓN

STORK'S BILL
DOVE'S FOOT
CROW FOOT
WILD ALUM ROOT
SPOTTED GERANIUM
CRANESBILL
WILD GERANIUM
CRANESBILL FAMILY
Geranium atropurpurem Heller

Geraniaceæ

I now introduce you to *patita de león,* so named by the Spanish New Mexicans because the leaf resembles the pad of a lion's paw, and called dove's foot and crow foot by the English-speaking inhabitants because they saw in the leaves a similarity to the claws of those birds. It possesses strong

148

astringent properties, which doubtless gave rise to the appellation of wild alum root, and is the reason for its use in diarrhea and in the second stage of dysentery. At various times it has been employed whenever an astringent was indicated: for example, in hemorrhages, indolent ulcers, opthalmia, leucorrhœa, and hematuria.

Evidently the Ottawa and Chippewa Indians had discovered this peculiarity, for they took a decoction of the whole plant as an anti-dysenteric.

The Spanish New Mexicans consider it excellent for the preservation of the teeth, and chew its roots for this purpose.

PATITO DEL PAIS
PATITO DEL CAMPO

BUFFALO PEA   Lathyrus decaphyllus Pursh.
WILD PEA
PEA FAMILY   Leguminosæ

Patito literally means small duck, and if you pull the flower out of the calyx and hold it horizontally, you will find that you have in your hand a miniature floral duck of pinkish hue.

The Spanish New Mexicans take a teaspoonful of its ground fruit, and a teaspoonful of dry pulverized *contrayerba* root Kallstrœmia brachystylis), mix them, and spread them on the face for toothache or ulcerated tooth, for mumps, and for headache. They say that this reduces the swelling and relieves the pain. They also mix the peas with *habas* (horse beans), grind them together, add a little granulated sugar, and fill a cigarette paper with the powder which they blow into the throat of a tonsilitis patient.

PAZOTE, HIPAZOTE, EPAZOTE DE COMER

WORMSEED   Chenopodium ambrosioides L.
MEXICAN WORMSEED
MEXICAN TEA
GOOSEFOOT FAMILY   Chenopodiaceæ

While I was talking with the proprietor of a drug store in Santa Fé, we were interrupted by a rather short man, more sturdy of beard than of stature, whose eyes had gradually closed until they were now mere glittering slits in a sea of wrinkles because of their continual exposure to biting wind and blinding sun. He entered the establishment quietly and refused to talk with anyone except my interlocutor. He held in his hand a bulging flour sack which he carefully guarded as if it were full of gold. My interest was aroused immediately, and I pretended to busy myself with some purchase, while attempting to discover what the bag contained. After nearly fifteen minutes of heated conversation, the sack changed hands, and a shower of dry *pazote* leaves poured out into a drawer to replenish the store's supply. The former owner of this herbal wealth departed, as silently as he had come, and the purchaser turned to me and asked whether I had noticed what had happened, and whether I knew that many of the medicinal plants were handled in that manner. Having so learned that they were, I left richer in my understanding of the New Mexican herbal business.

The Spanish word *pazote* is a derivative of the ancient Aztec, *epazotl*. That Mexican people took a decoction of *pazote* roots to restrain dysentery and to dissipate inflammations, but the Maya texts, which refer to it as *lucum-xiu,* meaning worm plant or wormseed, say that it is an excellent vermifuge.

Spanish New Mexican women grow it in their gardens and chew and swallow its dry or fresh leaves with salt, in order to regulate catamenial distress and to relieve pains after child-

150

birth. This is used also to bring about abortion.

A tea may be made from the plant, and drunk with a little sugar to produce milk or to make the blood flow, or to counteract post-parturition pains.

Small suppositories, called *calillas,* are formed with the leaves and employed as an emmenagogue.

The powdered *pazote* leaves, mixed with salt and ground *yerbabuena* (spearmint), and bound together with Lenox soap are used as *pindolas* for appendicitis. When one of these has been placed in the rectum, the patient drinks hot water, and immediately afterward, the *médica* presses gently upon the appendix. The *pindola* should not be passed quickly, but must remain long enough to clear out the bowels, and remove the pus from the appendix. If the pain does not cease with one treatment it may be repeated three times.

A decoction of the plant is taken as a blood purifier and its seeds are employed in seasoning meats.

PAZOTILLO

HORSEWEED	Erigeron canadensis L.
FLEABANE	
PRIDE WEED	
COLT'S TAIL	
CANADA FLEABANE	
BUTTERWEED	
BITTERWEED	
ASTER FAMILY	Compositæ

This erigeron is a very common weed throughout the United States, and appears to thrive even where other weeds have failed. It may reach a height of seven feet if it finds a good cultivated field in which to grow, and produces small greenish-white flowers from June to September.

The Zuñi Indians crush the rays of its blossoms between their fingers and insert them into their nostrils to cure rhinitis. Sneezing results, and relief is soon secured, they affirm.

Spanish New Mexican maidens are a swarthy breed, living in a sunbaked land, and therefore one of their highest aims is the possession of a clear white complexion. Although I have been unable to find many herbal methods which accomplish this, one effort consists in mashing, then soaking *pazotillo* leaves in water, and rinsing the face with the strained liquid. After this has been allowed to dry, a coat of powder may be applied.

PEGAPEGA

BUENA MUJER   Mentzelia multiflora A. Gray
LOASA FAMILY   Loasceæ

The Spanish verb *pegar* means to stick, and therefore *pega-pega* literally is translated into English as, it-sticks-it-sticks. The Spanish New Mexicans are to be complimented upon their insistence that the plant's clinging nature be emphasized through repetition, for it not only has brittle leaves with barbed hairs that catch in one's clothes, but it also possesses a highly mucilaginous sap nearly as adhesive as resin.

The Spanish New Mexicans have another name for this plant, which is *buena mujer,* good woman, because it sticks to a man with such constancy. They rub the well-ground herb upon rheumatic limbs, and in order to relieve those who suffer from pains in the back, they thoroughly pulverize the *pega-pega* between their hands, make it into a *clastico* (poultice) with a little water and place it on the afflicted portions.

Zuñi Indians tell us that once when an impersonator of an anthropic god was wearing a sacred blanket, *pegapega* attached itself to the robe and the wearer could not shake off the burr, with the result that the impostor was apprehended and suitably punished. Thereafter, this plant was highly honored for its intervention.

The Tewa Indians, being of a practical nature, hare the legs of a young boy before he is put on a horse for the first time, and rub the gummy herb on his skin. His clothes are

152

replaced and he is allowed to mount. This treatment is supposed to give him a good grip and enable him to ride without falling.

PIEDRA AZUL

BLUE STONE
COPPER SULPHATE

The crystals of copper sulphate, which may be familiar to certain individuals only because they are effective cleansers of swimming pools, are purchased at the pharmacy by the Spanish New Mexicans and are employed in curing wheat before it is planted. They have found that it protects the grain against smut.

PIEDRA INFERNAL

LUNAR CAUSTIC
SILVER NITRATE

Silver nitrate has to be obtained at the pharmacy. Because of its active properties, it is used to burn off warts.

PIEDRA LUMBRE
PIEDRA ALUMBRE

ALUM STONE

If a Spanish New Mexican is suffering from a profuse nose bleed, he burns the alum stone, grinds it into a fine powder, and snuffs it up his nostrils. The *médicas* maintain that it will remove a cataract in the eye. They bake it in the oven until it becomes spongy, soak it in water, and strain the solution through three cloths. They then put two or three drops of the liquid in the eye every night, until the affliction has disappeared. This treatment is very painful and considerably reddens the eye, "but", they insist, "it does cure".

153

PINHUÉ
PINGUÉ

COLORADO RUBBER PLANT Hymenoxys floribunda A. Gray
ASTER FAMILY Compositæ

The *pinhué* only grows about one foot high at best, but its yellow-rayed flowers make up for any defect in stature it may possess.

Both the Tewa Indians and the New Mexican Spanish collect the roots, peel off the outer skin, and chew the inner pulp. This produces a kind of chewing gum, considered good for the teeth and stomach, but if masticated too frequently, it is said to close the throat.

Likewise *pingué* is dangerous to sheep as it will form balls of rubber in their stomachs. In an effort to supplement our rubber supply during the World War I, this plant was gathered in large quantities.

PINO REAL COLORADO

YELLOW PINE Pinus brachyptera Engelm.
  (Pinus engelmanni Torr.)
  (Pinus scopulorum Lemmon)
PINE FAMILY Pinaceæ

This is one of the most common mountain trees in New Mexico, and supplies the state with nearly two-thirds of its native timber. The older trunks, which frequently reach a height of over one hundred feet, are covered with an irregular segmented yellowish-brown bark, which the Spanish New Mexicans formerly gathered, soaked in barrels of water, and used to color cow hides after they had been tanned. At present, one can see many of these trees, on the Mescalero Apache Reservation, that have been killed by girdling, since the Indians have removed their bark in order to obtain an exudation of resin with which to coat their wicker water bottles. Matilda

Coxe Stevenson says, "The members of the order of Sword Swallowers of the Great Fire fraternity at Zuñi, eat the yellow pine's male cones at the close of their ceremony, if they desire male children". In times of famine the Indians have been known to eat the inner bark of this tree.

The older and more widely experienced *médicas* rub fresh sap from the tree on scaly skin, and upon smallpox postules. They prescribe the oil from the small resin blisters *(botijitas)* for liver spots on the face *(pano)*, and recommend its application to the skin with a small brush.

PIÑON

PINYON　　　　　　　　　　　　　　　Pinus edulis Engelm.
PINE FAMILY　　　　　　　　　　　　Pinaceæ

The *piñon* tree is a rather low-spreading, open-crowned evergreen, which grows in the scattered groves of cedars and junipers, or entirely by itself in the foothill regions of New Mexico. But although of insignificant size and dull color in the complete brillance of midday, at sunrise and sunset the shifting shadows which it casts on a tawny soil seem fluid to the eye under the constant change of accent, in the ever-varying distribution of light.

Everyone familiar with New Mexico is also acquainted with the innumerable double-tracked paths which branch off the more frequently-traveled roads, and which lead to the remote supplies of *piñon* wood. Each autumn the woodgatherers ascend these lonely byways to the *piñon* forests, and return to the towns and villages with their burden of winter firewood packed in cylindrical bundles around their patient *burros'* bodies.

The Indians as well as the Spanish regard the *piñon* as a potential fuel supply. They boil its gum with soft iron oxide, which may also be procured in the mountains, to prepare a black dye. The Tewa at Hano mend their broken water jars

155

and cover their earthenware canteens with the resin to make them watertight, much as eastern Forest Indians caulked their birchbark canoes with spruce gum. Both the Tewa and Zuñi apply the liquid resin to cuts and sores, in order to "keep the air out", and sell the hard gum to those who will chew it. The Zuñi Indians also take the needles for syphilis. After they have been chewed and swallowed, the patient drinks a large quantity of water, and runs about a mile. Then, upon his return, he is wrapped in several blankets and made to sweat profusely. In conjunction with this treatment, the ulcers are scraped with the finger-nail until they bleed, when powdered *piñon* gum is sprinkled over them.

The Spanish New Mexicans formerly mixed whiskey with the pitch and used it as a varnish, and now they boil two handsful of the needles in a quart of water with a little Mexican brown sugar, to make a decoction against syphilis. The liquid is allowed to stand out-of-doors all night, and the dose of one glass should be administered three times a day.

The Spanish conquerors of New Mexico were immediately impressed upon their arrival with the potential value of the *piñon,* and, according to Fray Alonso de Benavides, there was a lively trade in *piñon* nuts between New Mexico and México City during the early days of the occupation period. In his famous Memorial to the King of Spain (1630), Benavides particularly described these trees because "of their nuts so large and tender to crack and the trees and cones so small and the quantity so interminable".

The descendants of these haughty *conquistadores* abandon all other work which may be in progress when the cones open in October, and entire families go out to harvest the nuts. These are shaken on the ground and collected unless one is so fortunate as to find a pack-rat's nest where two or three gallons already have been assembled.

It is roundly affirmed that good crops are produced only every seven years, and as the amount of the harvest does vary considerably, the Spanish New Mexicans, to whom the nuts

156

are a staple food, attempt to conserve a sufficient amount to last them at least two years. The flavor is improved and the nuts keep in better condition if toasted before being stored. The people say that, if eaten raw, they will cause stomach pains, but evidently the coyotes are not troubled with such considerations, and when other food is not obtainable, they turn to the nuts for sustenance.

One of the most diverting sights in Santa Fé is the *piñon* nut vendor with his wares. There was an old man in particular, apparently blind, who leaned upon a polished stick shaken by the palsied hand that held it, and who guarded with the curve of his angular back a basket from which he dispensed, to the measure of a small jelly glass, his meagre supply of *piñon* nuts. Naturally, his chief customers were people who have none of their own, but at times, the lure of their flavor overcomes *piñon* addicts, and one delighted in seeing these skillful purchasers, through a mysterious combination of lip and teeth and tongue, succeed in cracking the shells on one side of their mouths, and ejecting them on the other, having extracted the meat during the transfer, with such expert facility that the rapid flow of conversation and the tide of jokes was in no way interrupted.

PITAJAYA

PITAHAYA   Echinosereus paucispinus Rümpler
PITAYA
CACTUS FAMILY   Cactaceæ

The cactus that is usually called *pitajaya* in New Mexico is Echinocereus paucispinus, although it is certain that the same name would be given to any species of Echinocereus. There are several of them in the state with a much greater abundance of longer spines than this plant, which is one of the rarer species.

It has violently red flowers and grows only from twelve to eighteen inches in height. The Spanish New Mexicans gather these blossoms and boil them in half a cup of water as a remedy against swelling and dropsy. The decoction should be taken three times a day to dissipate the affliction.

Misappropriation of the word *pitajaya* has resulted in a great deal of confusion, since it is applied by many writers to signify the organ, or giant, cactus. John G. Burke, in "Folk-foods of the Rio Grande Valley and Northern Mexico", an article in the "Journal of American Folklore" during 1895, gives us a further application of the term. "The *alicóchis*", he writes, "to which many people persist in giving the name of *pitahaya,* is a cactus, resembling the *biznaga,* or Turk's Head, but smaller, and growing close to the ground; it yields, in the early days of Summer, a fruit the size of a small plum, green in color, filled with fine black seeds; the skin is quite thin. This is generally regarded as the most delicious of all the wild fruits. It rivals the strawberry or the raspberry in delicacy of flavor and in the graciousness with which it submits to every mode of treatment. It seems to be equally good whether served raw, stewed, in pies and puddings, or in ice-cream; it makes an acceptable addition to juleps and lemonades".

PLUMAJILLO

MILFOIL
YARROW
SNEEZEWEED
OLD MAN
THOUSAND SEAL
NOSEBLEED
ASTER FAMILY

Achillea lanulosa Nutt.

Compositæ

The *plumajillo* has an erect flower stalk tipped with massed small white blossoms which arise from the feathery foliage spreading around its base—hence its Spanish name, meaning little feather.

Yarrow, so the ancient herbalists tell us, was governed by Venus, and was one of the witches' herbs brought to weddings to insure seven years' love. Even among the superstitious of

158

the present day, it is regarded as a most potent love-charm, especially if plucked by a lovelorn maiden from the grave of a young man.

The Zuñi Indians maintain that its leaves produce a cooler sensation, when applied to the skin, than those of any other plant. Consequently, before certain ceremonies of their secret fraternities, those who are to dance in fire, or take live coals in their mouths, chew its blossoms and roots and anoint their bodies with the mixture. For the same reason, they grind and mix the entire plant with water and apply it to burns.

The Spanish Californians still steep its leaves in water to prepare a healing application for cuts and bruises, and to stop the flow of blood—which may be the reason why the plant has the colloquial name of nosebleed.

On the other hand, Spanish New Mexicans have found different employment for the *plumajillo*. They grind and mix its dry leaves with those of the *lantén* (plantain) and put the substance in a glassful of boiling water. This is then drunk to reduce fever, as it is a "cold plant"; but if taken in large quantities it acts as a purge. Moreover, the dry flowers are swallowed with water twice daily to dissipate a cough, and a poultice is made from the entire plant for sprains and broken bones.

POLÉO

PENNYROYAL
MINT FAMILY

Mentha sp.
Labiatæ

In order to reduce a very high fever, this plant is mashed with vinegar and salt, and spread over the entire body, including the head.

After a miscarriage, a woman should eat the leaves.

The old Californian Spanish formerly mixed *poléo* with sage for the suppression of excessive mensis, and treated chronic catarrh in the following manner: The *inmortal* root (Asclepiodora decumbens Nutt.), the button-like seed pods

159

of *rosilla,* and the stems and leaves of *poléo,* were toasted together in the oven and then ground to the fineness of flour. This powder was mixed with suet and the resultant salve was rubbed on the forehead, about the nose, and even on the neck. Concomitantly with this treatment, the patient snuffed up his nose a tea made with *poléo* leaves, and the leaves, stems and root, of *inmortal.* This washed out the nostrils, and supposedly relieved the congestion.

The Moors, who conquered and held Spain for several centuries, and who contributed so much to our present medicinal knowledge, now use the *poléo* flowers for headaches and colds, and administer a decoction of the leaves to women after childbirth.

POLÉO CHINO

TICKWEED   Hedeoma oblongifolia (Gray) Heller
SQUAWMINT
PENNYROYAL
MINT FAMILY   Labiatæ

This member of the mint family has an erect branching stem which supports very small leaves and tiny bluish-purple flowers in axillary clusters. Its botanical name is a corruption of the Greek word, *hedysma,* meaning sweetness.

The Spanish New Mexicans chew the green *poléo chino* for their teeth and for stomach trouble, and take a decoction of the entire herb as an emmenagogue. Since it is a "cold plant", it is considered excellent in reducing fevers. For this purpose, the dry leaves are ground very fine, and a teaspoonful of the powder is mixed with a glass of cold water. The solution must be drunk every day or the desired cure will not be produced.

It was common practice to identify "humores" with the presence of fever, and during the sixteenth century in England the following instructions were highly recommended: "Penny-

160

royall, dronken with honied water warmeth the bodie, and
cutteth off the grosse humores, and driveth away all cold
shiverings".

POLÉO DEL PAIS
POLÉO GRANDE

MINT   Mentha canadensis L.
MINT FAMILY   Labiatæ

The ancients believed that mint would prevent milk from
curdling, and that if mixed with salt, it was a good antidote
against the bites of mad dogs; but the present Spanish New
Mexicans roundly assert that it is good for other purposes.

They pour a cup of boiling water onto a teaspoonful of
its leaves and allow them to steep for twenty minutes. When
it has cooled, they give the solution to children, instead of
water, to reduce their fever, or they also mix the ground dry
leaves with white vaseline and rub it all over an infant's body.
But if the increased bodily heat has caused pains in the region
of the neck, they compound dry mint leaves with *inmortal*
(Asclepiodora decumbens Nutt.), and rub them on the afflicted part. Both for minors and adults the dry leaves are ground
and a poultice is prepared from the powder with hot water
and placed on the back of the neck or on the chest in order to
dissipate a cold. Mint tea is considered an excellent stomachic, and its green leaves are often used to flavor many dishes.

POÑIL

APACHE PLUME   Fallugia paradoxa (Don) Endl.
ROSE FAMILY   Rosaceæ

This attractive plant is well worth cultivating for decorative purposes since it grows rapidly even without much attention, and produces, on the end of slender downy stalks,
an abundance of clear white flowers similar to the wild rose.

161

The clusters of plumose fruits, at first greenish, but later tinged with red, remain on the stems for some time, and are nearly as beautiful as the blossoms. The shrub commonly is distinguished by its extended feathery carpels which, when dry, give it the appearance of clustered miniature Indian war bonnets, leading to the popular name, Apache plume.

The women of San Ildefonso pueblo steep its leaves in water until soft, and wash their hair in the infusion to promote its growth, but Spanish New Mexican *mujeres* boil the roots and rinse their hair with the decoction, after a shampoo, to prevent it from falling.

In order to dissipate a cough that hangs on, *poñil* roots that are dug in September are boiled, and sugar is added according to personal preference. Then a large glass of the liquid is taken warm upon rising, and another before retiring, as well as a small glass immediately preceding each meal. Spanish descendants in New Mexico also mix its dry ground leaves with those of the *punche* (native tobacco), and rub them upon rehumatic joints.

Nor are its brilliant white blossoms neglected by the *médicas,* who compound, with the pulverized flowers, *mastranzo* leaves (horehound), flour, and water to form a paste with which they massage swollen parts of the body.

If, through some hapless circumstance, a New Mexican resident should become bewitched, and begin to waste away as a result of this curse, he must grind the plumes of *poñil* with some *sangre de venado* (the Dragon's Blood of commerce), and add to the powder a little Mexican rock salt and some soot that has been collected with a teaspoon from a fireplace. He must then put the preparation into the kind of wine that the *padre* takes before breakfast, and drink the entire solution. This will drive away any evil effects that the magic may have had upon him, and help him to recover his health.

162

PONSO
TANSÉ

GREAT TANSY
TANSY
BITTER BUTTONS
PARSLEY FERN
ASTER FAMILY

Tanacetum vulgare L.

Compositæ

"Tansie is hoate in the second degree, and dry in the third, as it doth well appeere by his strong smell and bitter taste". (Dodœns, "Historie of Plantes", London, 1578.)

The familiar tansy is indigenous to Europe, and was introduced into this country, where it has escaped from the confines of garden walls and has grown spontaneously along roadsides and by ditches. Its strong aroma and bitter taste are nearly as well known as its deeply imbricated dark green leaves and brilliant golden yellow flowers.

The New Mexican Spanish make a tea from its leaves, or chew them fresh or dry with a little salt as a stomachic, or for *torson en las tripas* (cramps). They also use it in the treatment of chills and fever, and drink a decoction of the plant for torpid liver.

Old-fashioned Americans consider the tansy an excellent general tonic, an emmenagogue and a diaphoretic.

POPOTÓN
SACATÓN

PORCUPINE GRASS
SLEEPY GRASS
GRASS FAMILY

Stipa vaseyi Scribn.

Gramineæ

It appears fairly evident that the words *popotón* and *sacatón* came from the Aztec *popotl* and *zacatl* respectively, and the former are applied locally to a tall, decorative grass that

163

grows rapidly when not consumed by stock, and does very well on land that has been overgrazed. The people in the Sacramento-White Mountain region refer to it as "sleepy grass" and maintain that it has a narcotic effect upon the animals that eat it, but that acclimatized stock will not touch it.

In Guatemala, the common highlands tall grass called *sacate* grows from immensely tough roots which are harvested laboriously and are used in manufacturing the ordinary scrubbing-brush.

The Spanish New Mexicans sometimes make brooms by binding *popote* stalks together, and often boil its roots in order to derive a tea that is good for kidney trouble. This decoction is administered in a bottle to animals, if they develop symptoms of the same complaint.

There is another variety called *popote,* upon which stock never feeds, and which is gathered in the autumn and sold from house to house, because it is so highly prized as material for besoms, and because bundles of it, after the seeds have been burned off the slender end, are almost exclusively used in the Spanish American homes instead of commercial brooms.

For centuries, the superstitious have associated brooms with witches, and the New Mexican Spanish believe that the *popote* can neutralize any harm the witches may seek to do, and in order to counteract their evil intentions, one must take half-inch pieces of *popote,* and tie them in a cross with thread. Then one must add a grain of rock salt, two cloves, and two grains of mustard, and sew them all together in a little cloth bag which must be worn about the neck, or buttoned over the left breast onto the underwear.

PUNCHE

TOBACCO

NIGHTSHADE FAMILY

Nicotiana torreyana Nels. & Mcbr.
(Nicotiana attenuata Torr.)
Solanaceæ

This variety of tobacco that is cultivated in tenderly-guarded patches by the Spanish New Mexicans is a cousin of the *datura* (thorn apple). It is not unlike the milkweed in appearance, though it has a richer foliage and is a little more thick-set.

The tobacco plant has always had a mystical import to American Indians, who considered it sacred, and who solemnly invoke its "soul-consoling smoke" as an offering to the powers that rule life. It was burned to appease the divine forces, or to invite their aid, but almost never taken as a matter of personal indulgence.

Spanish New Mexicans smoke it in cigarettes, which are rolled in brown paper or corn husks, as well as in pipes, and they also pulverize the leaves and use them as snuff. But besides furnishing a source of pleasurable relaxation, it forms the basis of numerous medicinal remedies.

If a cold settles in the chest, they grind a few of its leaves to a fine powder and mix them with a half teaspoonful of lard. At night, this preparation is placed on a piece of linen and bound onto the chest with flannel. In the event that rheumatism develops, they boil a handful of *punche* in a pail of water, and give the patient a sponge bath on the painful parts. Piles are treated with suppositories made with raw fat, a pinch of *punche,* and a little salt. For kidney trouble, the pulverized *punche* is mixed with the juice of the gum plant *(yerba del buey)*—which is extracted by putting the young herb in an oven—and tied over the affliction. If the new mother has pains, a little *romero* (rosemary) and *punche* are sprinkled over a square of silk, which is then folded, heated over live coals and applied. This treatment is repeated as often as necessary.

165

"Chewing tobacco, to those who do not habitually use it, stops toothache. Tobacco moistened and bound to the wound helps snake-bite, and has kept many a man alive until whiskey could be had. In the same way it is very effective in the case of insect or spider bites. It acts as a disinfectant upon a wound and will help stop bleeding. Puny, delicate children who do not grow as they should are often 'helped' by the use of tobacco. Chewing seems to be the orthodox method of use in such cases. The tobacco helps the digestion, and its poison seems to be needed by the system to work against the poison that prevents growth. The poison of tobacco will 'kill' jaundice. Tobacco smoke has many uses. Smoking is beneficial to very corpulent persons as it will make them 'spit away' their fat. The first time I remember seeing a baby with colic it was being doctored by blowing smoke under its clothes. Earache may be relieved by blowing smoke into the ear. This is done by blowing into the bowl of the lighted pipe when the stem is held to the affected ear. Finally, smoking is a practice likely to help one afflicted with fits". (Folk-say", 1929, p. 74)

PUNCHÓN
TOBACO CIMARRÓN

GORDOLOBO (Californian Spanish   Verbasum thapsus L.
VERBASCO (Modern Castilian)
CANDELARIA (Modern Castilian)
MULLEIN
VELVET DOCK
VELVET PLANT
FLANNEL LEAF
WOOD BLADE
TORCH WEED
HUNG WORT
FIGWORT FAMILY   Scrophulariaceæ

It has long been a belief that odors have a curious effect on morals, and at least one ancient writer has commented on "the peculiar wickedness of people who lived in the neighborhood of Etna and Vesuvius"—a characteristic he connected with the sulphurous discharges from these volcanos, and to which Shakespeare alluded in "Hamlet" when he wrote:

> *"Be thou a spirit of health or goblin damn'd,*
> *Bring with thee airs from heaven or blasts*
> *from hell?"*

Therefore, fumigations and perfumes formerly played an extensive part in evocatory magic; and, on the authority of Agrippa, mullein leaves, because of their frogrance, were reserved to dispel demons, upon which they had a strong effect. This attitude doubtless was continued at least until the close of the Middle Ages, for the people of medieval Europe scathingly referred to mullein as "hag-taper", since it was employed by witches in their incantations.

The early Greeks and Romans made lampwicks from the dried mullein stalks by dipping them in tallow, and it may have been through remembrance of this Roman custom that the Spaniards named it *candelaria,* and the English, torchweed. Botanists of the seventeenth and eighteenth centuries knew that their contemporaries considered the figwort group of plants excellent in the treatment of scrofula, and consequently gave the family its present identification .

The Spanish always have been able to amplify their impressive language through the implications permitted by the addition of a prefix or a suffix, and those of Spanish origin in New Mexico, recognizing a similarity of appearance and utility between the *punche* (native tobacco) and the larger mullein, have called it *punchón,* great *punche* plant. As a substitute for tobacco they dried smoked the *punchón* leaves in cigarettes wrapped with corn husks. The old manner of making such cigarettes consisted in cutting the dry corn husks into the desired size, and then manipulating them until they were sufficiently soft easily to enclose the crumbled leaf.

Early Californians used the mullein externally in pulmo-

167

nary diseases and sprains. Spanish New Mexicans say that, besides being pleasurable, the inhaled smoke from these cigarettes is good for asthma; and that the mullein leaves soaked in *mula blanca* (local corn whiskey) make a beverage that is also beneficial in counteracting this same complaint.

During the North American Civil War, in the Confederate States lung troubles were treated with a syrup made from mullein leaves and cherry bark, as the high cost and great scarcity of commercially-produced medicines forced all those living on the land to turn to medicinal herbs for assistance.

QUELITE SALADO
QUELITES SALADOS

LAMB'S QUARTERS   Chenopodium album L.
WHITE GOOSEFOOT
PIGWEED
GOOSEFOOT FAMILY   Chenopodiaceæ

This familiar weed of gardens, waste places, roadsides, and unkept fields, is an immigrant from England, as is, according to R. A. C. Prior, the author of "On the Popular Names of British Plants", its name of lamb's quarters, presumably a corruption of "Lammas quarter", an ancient festival in the English calendar.

During the springtime, Spanish New Mexicans gather and cook the *quelite salado* leaves as "greens", and sometimes, to give them more flavor, add a few *chile* seeds to the dish.

I was immensely pleased when I discovered that the Moors, who have had such lasting contacts with the Spanish, also cook the leaves of the same plant in a variety of ways, and greatly enjoy them as a green vegetable. Their name for it is *qliql,* strangely similar to the former Aztec word which was *quilitl.*

Seeds of the different species of Chenopodium were formerly collected by the Indians, ground or parched, and used in making cakes or porridge.

168

QUELITES YUS
QUELITES COLORADO YUS

PIGWEED   Amaranthus powellii S. Wats.
AMARANTH
AMARANTH FAMILY   Amaranthaceæ

This plant is a brother of the *alegría* and the *chile puerco*.

The Spanish New Mexicans eat its oblong leaves in the early spring as "greens", but they maintain that when the herb is older and bearing seeds, it is poisonous for people and pigs, but not for cows.

QUESO

CHEESE

Early accounts of medicinal practices in old California reveal that a poultice of any available kind of melted cheese was formerly used for the bites of scorpions and other insects, and I discovered that this practice still prevails in New Mexico as a remedy against rattlesnake bites.

RAMA DE SABINA
(Juniper branch)

ONE-SEEDED JUNIPER   Juniperus monosperma (Engelm.) Sarg.
COMMON CEDAR
CYPRESS FAMILY   Cupressaceæ

This is the common juniper of New Mexico. It is a multiple-branched, scraggy tree, some twelve to twenty-five feet high, with gray stringy bark, rather yellowish-green leaves, and small blue fruit with a sweet, resinous taste.

At Hano, the Tewa Indians fumigate a lying-in woman the fourth day after parturition with the branches and leaves placed in a vessel on hot coals. More generally, the leafy twigs, after being toasted over embers, are bound tightly onto a bruise or sprain to reduce the swelling and pain. Among the Zuñi Indians, *rama de sabina* is roasted in a fireplace, then steeped in hot water, and the tea is drunk by the women to promote muscular relaxation before parturition. This type of decoction is also taken after childbirth to hasten the cessation of catamenia.

As if in accordance with the Indian practice, Spanish New Mexican women, a month before childbirth, make a tea by boiling the juniper twigs and drink half a cup every morning. In order to reduce inflammation of the stomach, and as my informant put it, "to take the cold out", one must cut the tender ends of juniper branches, and cover them with two large cupsful of water. This is boiled until one cupful of liquid remains, when it is strained and allowed to stand over night. Half a cup should be taken every morning. A somewhat different method is employed in the treatment of *torsón en las tripas* (gripes in the intestines). The twigs are mashed and hot water is poured over them. The liquid is strained off and drunk every morning for three days.

REMOLINO

In Spanish, *remolino* means a whirlwind, a whirlpool, or a cowlick, but in New Mexico this word has an additional application and refers to the nests of the Mason bee, which are made with pebbles fastened together by resin, and filled with honey for the young insects.

These cells are collected, roasted and ground, mixed with a little water, and drunk for flatulency or suppression of mensis.

ROMERILLO

SILVER SAGE   Artemisia filifolia Torr.
ASTER FAMILY   Compositæ

The silver sage, a blood relation of *mariola, anisote,* and *estafiate,* has selected mountain slopes upon which to live, and scorns the lowly plains graced by its cousins.

Spanish Californians say of another species of Artemisia known to them by this vernacular name. They drink a cup of *romerillo* tea every morning, and every evening at bedtime, for forty days, to effect a cure, and also apply a poultice to the chest and back every night. This is prepared by wilting the leaves of *romerillo* in warm ashes and by putting them in a woolen cloth with a little olive oil. It is absolutely necessary that both the cloth and its contents be warm when applied. They maintain that salt and any greasy food should be denied asthmatic patients during this period of treatment.

Silver sage is a favorite remedy with the New Mexican Tewa Indians and those at Hano, Arizona. They chew and swallow it with water, or drink it in a hot decoction for indigestion, flatulency, and biliousness. In addition, they compress on the stomach a bundle of the plant that has been steeped in boiling water and wrapped in a cloth, to drive away pains.

Spanish New Mexicans employ it in the same way as the Tewa and for the same purposes; and furthermore boil the entire bush in water to make a bath for rheumatism. The *penitentes* wash their lacerated back with *romerillo* tea which acts as an astringent.

One informant at Taos had an extremely high regard for the *romerillo,* since, according to her, "it is really good for everything".

ROMERILLO DEL LLANO

Initiated *medicas* maintain that if a decoction of this un-identified plant is made from the leaves and taken before meals and at bed time, in small doses, it will have a salutory action on pain in the stomach or on distended stomach, through stimulation of the bowels.

ROMERO DE CASTILLA

COSTMARY   Chrysanthemum balsamita L.
ASTER FAMILY   Compositæ

Romero de castilla is a far less common member of the Aster group.

When boiled with the crushed meats and shells of pecan nuts until a strong tea results, this herb makes an excellent mouthwash.   It has even greater significance in treatment for hemorrhages of the uterus.   A quart of native red wine is boiled with a handful of *romero;* an ordinary brick is heated quite hot, put in a vessel, and covered with the liquid.   The patient, who has been wrapped in a sheet, stands over the steam until relief is obtained.

ROSA CIMARRON
ROSA DEL CAMPO (Sencilla)

WILD ROSE   Rosa fendleri Crépin
ROSE FAMILY   Rosaceæ

The wild rose in New Mexico hedges many a field which otherwise would have no verdure to grace its borders.   It braves great altitudes, fringing the streams and spreading over the mountainsides up to the timber line.

The petals are collected, dried, packed in bags and hung on the *vigas.*   When winter colds bring sore throats the finely-ground petals mixed with a little sugar are placed in a paper

172

tube and blown into the patient's throat. For a severe case, this treatment is repeated every two or three hours and is said to give great relief. Another method consists in mixing the same powder with butter which is swallowed four times a day. Even in Culpeper's time our ancestors in England used honey of roses in gargles and lotions to wash sores, either in the mouth or throat.

In regard to skin troubles, think twice before having eczema, and if your decision is favorable carefully select a wildcat and extract his fat. Mix this with ground rose petals and apply the ointment two or three times a day.

The dry powder also is used as a healing application for fever blisters.

It is claimed that the old-fashioned red garden rose gives even better results than *rosa cimarron*.

J. P. Harrington says that at Santa Clara pueblo the Indians dry rose petals and keep them in their houses as an agreeable perfume. For mouth sores a salve is made of finely-ground petals mixed with grease.

"A popular home remedy among the Indians, just as it is among us, is the purgative. One day when I called on an Aztec Indian friend, she explained that they were not having much to eat because her son 'was in physic'. She had given him the water of boiled roses of Castile. The dose was to be repeated for several days, and the whole family were thoughtfully abstaining from eating certain indigestible foods, such as meat, during the period".—("Mexican Folkways" 1925).

ROSA DE CASTILLA

OLD-FASHIONED RED ROSE   Rosa sp.
ROSE FAMILY   Rosaceæ

"The rose is the flower of love, poetry, grace, and beauty, dyed in many hues by the nectar of the gods. Sirups, honeys, conserves, oils and essences made from the rose crowd the pages of the old 'herbals' to 'comfort the brayne and the heart and quicken the spyrte.' "

As if in remembrance of the rose's fabled healing properties, the Spanish New Mexicans, in order to alleviate that troublesome complaint—a sore throat—swallow, four times a day, a mixture of powdered rose petals, sugar and butter.

Even the Moors believe that to smell this aromatic flower stimulates the heart; and with quiet scorn for the soothing effects of commercial linaments, they allow the rose petals to stand in the sun, soaking in olive oil, and thus make a healing application for pains in the back.

ROSA DE CASTILLA

PERSIAN YELLOW ROSE   Rosa sp.
ROSE FAMILY   Rosaceæ

The yellow *rosa de castilla* probably originally came from Persia through the gardens of the Moors, and in New Mexico has "gone native" along the roadsides and *acequias* (irrigation ditches).

Descendants of those Spanish colonials who first introduced it into the Southwest shower the paths of their saints in procession on holy days with the fragrant rose leaves; and when one of the family is suffering from fever, they strive to alleviate the illness by boiling the dry or fresh petals in water until it turns yellow, and administer the decoction with a little sugar after it has cooled.

In and around Canjilón, dried powdered leaves of the *rosa de castilla* are swallowed without liquid for wintertime attacks of sore throat.

ROSETA

SAND BUR   Cenchrus pauciflorus Benth.
GRASS FAMILY   Gramineæ

The Spanish New Mexicans call this plant *roseta,* or rosette, presumably from the sprayed appearance of its terminal
burs, whose spines are sharp and strong enough to pierce
the uppers of shoes, and which usually break off when an
attempt is made to extract them from one's flesh, leaving
an intensely painful wound. It is one of the most pernicious
and persistent weeds of the state, and appears to take particular pleasure in growing in alfalfa fields, where it will soon
cause great damage to the crop unless eradicated, as stock
cannot eat fodder containing the burs.

A decoction of the entire plant is used in the preparation
of blue cornmeal mush, and it is also given to nursing mothers
to increase their lactation.

ROSITA MORADA

ALPINE PINK   Phlox nana Gray
PHLOX FAMILY   Polemoniaceæ

This member of the phlox family is esteemed highly by
the Spanish New Mexicans as a remedy against fever blisters.
The dry petals are ground and powdered on the sore.

Formerly, a purplish-red dye for woolen stockings, serapes,
blankets, and other garments was made by steeping a quantity
of the whole plant in tepid water. The spun wool then was
soaked in the dye for eight days, after which, the wool was
removed and dried in the hot sun over an old cloth-covered
bed spring, as this permitted free circulation of air to all parts
of the wool. Only a shortage of good coloring matter led the
settlers to use this formula for dye, as it brought sadly fugitive
results.

RUDA

RUE   Ruta graveolens L.
RUE FAMILY   Rutaceæ

Since the time of Hippocrates this soothing herb has been known; probably it has been familiar since before 450 B. C. It is a native of Southern Europe and is grown in many gardens throughout the United States. The specimens that I have were collected above Río del Medio, high in the Sangre de Cristo range, where evidently it has become naturalized along the borders of a small stream. The dry leaves imported from México can be bought in *boticas,* or pharmacies.

> *Para curar la sordera*
> *No hay como la ruda*
> *Y para decir que no*
> *No hay como quedarse muda.*
>
> *As a cure for the deaf*
> *There's nothing like rue,*
> *And as a way to say no*
> *There is nothing like silence.*

Renowned even in local verse, this remedy for deafness is very simple. The desiccated leaves are made into a cigarette and the smoke is blown into the patient's ear.

Used as a sedative, a half-teaspoonful of *ruda* is mixed with enough tobacco for fifteen cigarettes and smoked to quiet the nerves. A cigarette of the pure leaves is smoked for neuralgia, and for earache a few leaves are heated with several drops of oil and applied. Again a cigarette is used if one is suffering from *"destemplamiento de la cabesa"* (headache due to a cold); in addition a little of the plant is sprinkled on live coals and the smoke inhaled. Undisturbed sleep follows this treatment, especially if a pillow made of the plant is used. A cup of *ruda* tea is supposed to relieve the much-abused *estomago,* for, as we know, delicious though *chili* and beans may be, they are not always kind to the stomach.

176

It is not surprising to find that rue has an almost universal reputation. In fact, we know positively that it was esteemed throughout Europe, Asia, and North Africa. In Arabic it is called *rowta,* and in Morocco at the present time another species of the same plant (Ruta chalepensis L.), is used as follows: the odor of the crushed leaves is inhaled by nervous people for the calming effect, and oil in which the leaves have been cooked is dropped into the ear to relieve inflammation.

Culpeper, early in 1700, recommended Ruta graveolens for many ailments and the following quaint recipe is another link in our chain: "The juice warmed in a pomegranate shell or rind, and dropped into the ears, helps the pains of them".

RUDA DE LA SIERRA
RUDA CIMARRON

MEADOW RUE   Thalictrum fendleri Engelm.
CROWFOOT FAMILY   Ranunculaceæ

This *ruda* readily overcomes whatever inconspicuousness it may have because of an insignificant height, by a singular delicacy and grace, achieved through a shower of pale yellow stamens, with purplish filaments which fall from the center of its four greenish-white sepals, forming so many little floral tassels at the end of its tender-leafed stems. There are no petals.

At Río del Medio, for *destemplamiento de la cabesa* (when the head aches and feels congested after a cold), a cigarette is made from the herb and smoked, or a little of the plant is sprinkled on live coals and the smoke is inhaled. After the latter treatment, the head is placed on a pillow of the dry leaves so that the cure may be completely effectual.

In Elizabethan England, meadow rue evidently was considered quite powerful, as contemporary directions say that "the iuyce of wilde Rue mengled with Hony, wine, the iuyce of fenill, and the gaule of a Henne, quickeneth the sight, and remoueth al clowdes and the pearles in the eyes. Also the wilde Rue hath the like virtue as the Rue of the garden, but it is of greater force, in-so much as the auncient Physitions would not use it, because it was so strong, saving about the diseases and webbes of the eyes in manner as is aboue writen".

SABINA MACHO
PINO MACHO

MULE PINE
PROSTRATE JUNIPER
CYPRESS FAMILY

Juniperus sibirica Burgsd.

Cupressaceæ

Sabina macho is a dwarf evergreen which seldom grows over two feet high, but which is something of a "family" plant as it bands together in moderate and dignified clumps to repel the growth of any "foreign'" weed that might wish to settle in its midst.

Spanish New Mexicans drink a decoction of its dry or fresh leaves for fever or thin blood; and boil a small piece of its short branch to make a hot tea for stomachache or colic.

SANGRE

BLOOD

The blood of various animals has been employed in charms and necromancy ever since man became a thinking creature, and he has long sought to attain the strength of his kill by eating its heart or drinking its blood. Spanish New Mexicans evidently have retained a portion of this belief, since they take the fresh blood of a cow, calf, or sheep, stir, and drink it for tuberculosis. They maintain that the cure will be much more effective if the treatment can be given daily.

According to the author of an article on "Animal Fats in Folk-medicine", which appeared in the 1929 issue of "Folk-say", there still obtains in Oklahoma another phase of such an attitude and custom. He declares that a child suffering from "fits" may be cured (or so the initiated say) by thrusting its feet into the opened body of a freshly-killed chicken. The cure is more "powerful" if the chicken be cut open while it is alive, and the child's feet placed into it before the chicken is dead. The dying of the chicken with the child's feet in its body seems to have something to do with the cure. "Only once", he concludes, "did I have the explanation that the warmth of the chicken's body drew out the fits".

SANGRE DE VENADO

RATTAN PALM   Calamus Draco
PALM FAMILY   Palmaceæ

Sangre de venado literally means venison blood, but it is in fact the Dragon's Blood of commerce, obtained particularly from the red resin of the Malayan rattan palm, Calamus draco, or from one or two other species of Calamus, and utilized extensively as a varnish colorant and in photo-engraving.

Spanish New Mexicans purchase it at the pharmacies and employ it in the treatment of paralysis. They mix a large piece of ground *sangre de venado* with a handful of dried *barbasco* (croton weed), one-half teaspoon of cinnamon, and one-half teaspoon of nutmeg. A small portion of this preparation is stirred in one-half glass of warm water and given to the patient. The remainder is made into a paste with olive oil and rubbed on the paralyzed members. The patient must be put in bed as soon as both remedies have been given, and forced to sweat profusely.

When mixed with one teaspoonful of ground *azahar* (orange blossoms), wine, and *hueso de licor,* Dragon's Blood is drunk two or three times a day for *aire en el pecho (aire"* usually means neuralgia or shooting pains).

179

It was an old belief that a piece of *sangre de venado,* wrapped in paper and thrown on the fire, restored love to a deserted maiden if she repeated while it was burning:

"May he no pleasure or profit see
Till he comes back again to me".

SIEMPREVIVA

STONECROP   Sedum sp.
ORPINE FAMILY   Grassulaceæ

Siempreviva, or the ever-living, is a tender plant with thick light-green leaves and multiple stems that is grown in nearly every native house, and cherished there for its beauty and because of its gift for relieving pain.

When earache arises in a Spanish New Mexican family, one of the *siempreviva* leaves is heated and placed in the ear, or if someone should suffer from corns, a leaf is crushed and bound on them; and if backache arises, perhaps as a result of constant hard work, a handful of these leaves is mashed, then heated and poulticed on the back.

SOCOYOL

CHOCOYLE (Mora)   Oxalis violacea L.
JOCOYOL (Mexican Spanish)
VIOLET WOOD-SORREL
WOOD SORREL
SHAMROCK
TREFOIL
WOOD-SORREL FAMILY   Oxalidaceæ

This is a small perennial herb with a creeping rootstock, numerous radical leaves, and rose-purple flowers. It is inodorous and has a pleasantly acid taste, due to its content of oxalic acid. There is, therefore, complete consistency in deriving both the term of oxalic acid and the botanical name of *oxalis* from the Greek word, *oxys,* meaning sour.

The "Salts of Sorrel", formerly so widely-used to remove

ink spots and iron marks from linen, are merely the salt of this acid that has been removed from the *socoyol.*

Spanish New Mexicans enjoy its acidity and eat the raw plant. One the other hand, they sometimes boil two or three teaspoonsful of the green or dry leaves in a cup of water and take the decoction in the morning as a vermifuge.

TECOMACA

Tecomaca is the commercial gum elemi that is derived in the Philippine Islands from Canarium commune L., in Venezuela and Brazil from Protium Carana Humb., and in Yucatán from Amyris Plumieri DC. It is a resinous gum obtained by incising the trees at the time they are developing new leaves. It is a diaphanous substance, unctuous to the touch, with a warm, bitter taste, and a strong odor resembling a mixture of lemon and fennel. Although its color varies, it is usually greenish with intermingled points of white or yellow.

Naturally, the Spanish New Mexicans cannot gather this exudation, and have to purchase it at the pharmacy. They place it on the temples for headache and neuralgia, apply it to boils to reduce the swelling, and affirm that it will draw splinters from the skin.

TECONBLATE

BUCKTHORN FAMILY

Condalia spathulata A. Gray
Rhamnaceæ

The *teconblate* occurs chiefly on the mesas of the southern part of New Mexico, particularly around Tularosa, and often appears to be merely a bush composed of spines. It may be recognized, however, by its younger branches, which always are bluish-green, even after the leaves have fallen. Sometimes its fruit is eaten, but though the seeds are very large, the amount of pulp comparatively is quite small, so that it enjoys only limited favor as an article of diet.

181

On the other hand it is more highly-regarded as a remedy against tubercular cough, or a bad cough arising from a cold, both of which are treated by drinking, three times a day, a decoction of small pieces of the plant.

TEQUESQUITE

Tequesquite is a crude sodium bicarbonate which forms on the borders of mineral springs in New Mexico, and which is also found near several lakes of the state.

New Mexican *cocineras,* when they want to make the cakes known as *marquesotes* and *supiros* especially light and fluffy, substitute *tequesquite* for the commercial article as a baking powder, and sometimes add it to *chile* as a preventive against heartburn.

When children develop distended stomach as a result of an unusual amount of gas, they are given a few drops of *tequesquite* mixed with hot water at every meal, and when adults suffer from the same cause, they drink a preparation of one-half teaspoonful of this soda in one-half glass of warm water, immediately before retiring.

THE EFFICACIOUS DEAD

Not all cures are worked by plants. In medieval England, hangmen made a business, for fees, of admitting several persons at a time to the scaffold at executions, as wens and goiters were commonly believed to be curable by the "dead touch". In fact, Thomas Hardy found this superstition so common in Wessex that he based his tale of "The Withered Arm" upon this theme.

Evidently the Spanish New Mexicans have entertained a similar attitude, preserving it up to the present, for an informant told me, "Women who have no children often have *papera* (goiter). This can be easily remedied by laying the hand of the patient on a cold corpse for twenty minutes, then placing the cold hand on her throat. The goiter is certain to be cured and to disappear".

TIERRA BLANCA

Tierra blanca, or white earth, is a particular kind of soil found at Cerro Gordo; it is used as a powder on the face to prevent sunburn. It is soaked in cold water for twenty-four hours; then the water is thrown away, and the residue is formed into small sakes and dried. They may be kept for some time in this condition and utilized whenever necessary.

TIERRA DE RATA

Tierra de rata is the earth that has been brought up by gophers and that can be obtained from the mounds beside their holes. If you mix one-third of a cup of this earth with two-thirds of a cup of water, and employ the preparation as a mouthwash, you will be using a remedy that Spanish New Mexicans believe to be especially beneficial in counteracting pyorrhœa.

TIERRA DE NUESTRO SEÑOR DE ESQUIPULA

Among the ancients, earth was long respected for its healing qualities; and, combined with a good measure of faith, it produced results which have justified its continued use in folk cures.

Long before the Spanish conquered, so the Indians say, there was a boiling spring of sand near Chimayo, which never ceased to bubble, and which never lacked for sand. And the family of Bernardo Abeyta, a very religious Spaniard, came

183

and settled on this venerable spot. Now Señor Abeyta did penance the year around, but especially during Lent. Often he could not sleep at night, so deep were his devotions, and he went out into the open and prayed and scourged himself. One evening, he saw a vision of Our Lord of Esquipula, who commanded him to build a *Sanctuario*. Accordingly, a native artist carved an image of the holy apparition, and the Sanctuario de Nuestro Señor de Esquipula de Chimayó was erected directly over the ground so sacred in Indian belief. Ever since, the faithful have journeyed to this shrine, proffered their votive offerings, and taken away with them some of the earth from a cavity in the vestry floor, since this sand is good for everything. In case of high wind a pinch cast into the burning fireplace will overcome the wind, even as ordinary sand extinguishes fires. And a little of it put in the throat with water is good for the tonsils, or a spoonful of water with a pinch of the sand helps babies who are teething.

There is another story of a more unscrupulous owner of this chapel who set out upon a business trip, hoping to combine profit with benevolence. He loaded several burros with his blessed *tierra,* and took the road to Colorado. His panniers emptied rapidly while his pockets filled with coins, and before long he found himself faced by the necessity of replenishing his stock. To return home would consume valuable time and mean the loss of considerable profit. Upon reflection, he realized that Colorado earth would admirably serve his need—which indeed it did—until one dark night he disappeared from the region for his own good.

TOLOACHE

CHAMISO (Spanish)
ESTRAMONIO (Spanish)
THORN APPLE
ANGEL TRUMPET
JIMSON WEED
JAMESTOWN WEED
MAD APPLE
DEVIL'S APPLE
APPLE OF PERÚ
NIGHTSHADE FAMILY

Datura meteloides DC. and
Datura stramonium L.

Solanaceæ

Datura meteloides is a native of México and Southwestern United States, but the origin of Datura stramonium is disputed; perhaps it comes from the Asiatic continent. The Sanskrit *dhattura* and the Hindustani *dhatura* form the basis of the general name. When Hernando Cortés entered the elaborate Aztec gardens of Mexico, he and his followers were amazed at their beauty and the variety of cures effected by their varied herbs, among which was the datura, used to alleviate all bodily pains. It was then known as *toloatzin* (inclined head) on account of its nodding capsules. This became modified to *tolache*, and used for several distinct species of *datura*. The post-conquest Maya, who called this plant *Mehen-x-toh-ku*, applied it mashed with butter to reduce tumors.

The Aztec, however, were not the only Indians who knew *toloache*, for the Zuñi tell us that long ago, when they still dwelt in the underworld, a boy and girl found a trail up to this world of light, and decorated their heads with garlands of the large, white, sweet-smelling flowers while walking upon the earth. But these adventurous journeys were their undoing, for they met the Twin Sons of the Sun Father, the Divine Ones, to whom they joyously poured forth what they had learned—that they knew how to put people to sleep and to make them see ghosts; that they could make others walk about and detect thieves. The Divine Ones, deeply alarmed, decided the two children should be taken away. So the couple disappeared into the earth forever, but where they vanished

185

flowers sprang up like those the boy and girl had worn on their heads.

Even now the Zuñi use *toloache* for purposes similar to those suggested by the mythical children. A small quantity of the powdered root of Datura meteloides is administered by the rain priest to cause one to go to sleep and see ghosts. This procedure seeks rain, and "rains will surely come the day following the taking of the medicine, unless the man to whom it is given has a bad (evil) heart".

The Zuñi Indians employ Datura stramonium as a narcotic, anodyne, and anesthetic, and the blossoms and roots ground to a powder as an external application for wounds and bruises. In México it is sold as a love potion.

Mary Austin describes, in the "Land of Little Rain", how a decoction of datura is given by Paiute mothers to their daughters when they are put to the strain of the three-day courting dance—which, if undergone successfully, leads to their proper engagement. If the girl fails, however, her marriage is postponed for another year.

Nor were the effects of this powerful plant entirely limited to Indians, for Robert Beverly, in "History and Present State of Virginia" (1705), amusingly describes its results upon a group of soldiers who had made a boiled dish of its early shoots, believing them to be edible herbs: "Some of them ate plentifully of it", he writes, "the Effect of which was a very pleasant Comedy; for they turn'd natural fools upon it for several days: One would blow up a feather in the Air; another would dart Straws at it with much Fury; another, stark naked, was sitting in a Corner, like a Monkey, grinning and making mows at them; a Fourth would fondly kiss and paw his companions and swear in their faces with a Countenance more antik than any Dutch Doll . . . A thousand such simple Tricks they play'd, and after Eleven Days, returned to themselves again, not remembering anything that had pass'd". Beverly refers to the plant as Jamestown weed, from which the name Jimson weed is doubtless derived.

186

An old woman at Arroyo Seco, New Mexico, whose husband allegedly had been blinded by lightning and cured by brandy, told me of a little orphan girl, whose hair, in spite of all experimentation, persisted in housing a generous colony of lice. In desperation, her foster parents ground *toloache* seeds, mixed them with fat, and rubbed the salve on her head. Like magic the colony vanished. And when a Domingo Indian was told of this miraculous cure, he exclaimed, "Oh! a much better remedy is rabbit's milk!" Needless to say, the author, never having tried this, disclaims all responsibility for its use.

An ointment of the ground seeds and suet is rubbed on boils, pimples, and swellings; the powdered leaves are applied to piles; and hot baths containing the plant give relief to colds and diarrhœa.

During the first World War, Datura stramonium was cultivated in the United States as a substitute for atropine.

The dry leaves sometimes are smoked to relieve spasmodic asthma.

"In Mexico today there is a current belief, especially with the peons, who are the direct descendants of the Aztecs, that the unbalanced mind of the miserable Carlotta, widow of the unfortunate Maxmilian, was not due to the misfortunes of her husband, which her Christian faith and resignation would have enabled her to endure, but was caused by a decoction of talavatchi administered by Indian women. The action of this herb, the administration of which was one of the sciences of the Aztecs, is to destroy the mind but not the body. In the Empress' case, although she is possessed of excellent bodily health, outside of an interest shown in flowers, the world to her does not exist. The love of home, country, and friends, passed away after the draught of the old Indian witch's decoction". ("Touring Topics", January, 1930. "Medicine and Surgery Among the First Californians", by Cephas L. Bard, M. D.)

TOMATE DEL CAMPO

GROUND TOMATO
GROUND CHERRY
GARDEN HUCKLEBERRY
NIGHTSHADE FAMILY

Physalis neomexicana Rydb.

Solanaceæ

This plant is a common inhabitant of desert washes, mesas, and stony hillsides throughout New Mexico, and develops capsules like a papery envelope enclosing a small fruit resembling a diminutive tomato. It has therefore been called *tomato del campo,* the tomato of the plains, by the Spanish descendants, who mix either the ground green or ripe fruit with a pinch of salt, and compress it on the throat for tonsil trouble.

The Plains Indian women stewed the berries with honey or whatever substitute for sugar they might have, from which custom the pioneers learned to make them into jam. And to this day, seed catalogues intended for the Plains states, where fruit is scarce, advertise the seeds under the name of garden huckleberry to be grown for preserving.

TOMATILLO DEL CAMPO
TOMATITO PELON

TOMATILLO (Tularosa)
TOMATITO (Cienega)
BULL NETTLE
NIGHTSHADE FAMILY

Solanum elæagnifolium Cav.

Solanaceæ

"Since the days of Adam, the renown of the nightshades has encircled the globe. The henbanes decorating the tombs and crowning the victor, the daturas spreading from pole to pole and ever carrying enchanting love; the ever-wonderful belladona (beautiful lady), sinister, austere, shade-loving plants appearing as weeds, shrubs and trees, born of the gods and the angels, the stars and the witches, intoxicating, deadly, carrying in their sap the poison of the savage, the Borgias, sorcerers, and kings".

188

The Solanum elæagnifolium is a silvery member of this august company. It has greyish leaves that curve downward from its branched stems like so many scimiters, and it is formidably armed with unobtrusive but extremely sharp spines. It produces a berry that is green when it first develops, but which later turns dark and then yellow as it dries. In general appearance it roughly resembles a small tomato, which accounts for the varied diminutives of the Spanish given this plant by Spanish New Mexicans. It might be added here that the Nahuatl word, *tomatl,* is the root of both the present English and Spanish terms, although the first European name applied to the vegetable tomato by the Spaniards in South America was *manzana del amor,* or love apple. These early Spanish explorers were the first to introduce tomatoes into Europe, where formerly they were peeled and eaten apple fashion. Strangely enough, the name "love apple" now is given to the daturas, showing how time and peoples change their nomenclatures and borrow those of others.

The *tomatillo* berries serve as a substitute for rennet in curdling milk and producing clabber. When green, they are crushed, mixed with salt and bound on the throat for swollen tonsils, but after they have dried and turned yellow, they are ground, the powder is placed on a cigarette paper, and blown into the throat as a remedy against tonsilitis, catarrah, and headache.

Zuñi Indians put the chewed root in the cavity of an aching tooth, and regard goat's milk curdled with the berries as a particularly delicious beverage.

TOMATITO

TOMATOES (Arroyo Seco, Taos)   Solanum nigrum L.
BLACK NIGHTSHADE
NIGHTSHADE FAMILY   Solanaceæ

This member of the nightshade family is much less aggressive than Solanum elæagnifolium, since it lacks the latter's spines, and seeks to hide under a darker green foliage a very sweet and quite palatable black fruit, about the size of a blueberry. These the New Mexican children especially enjoy eating, and strangely enough, they are free to indulge themselves, since the well-known deadliness of the Nightshade family is absent in this plant when ripe.

TORNILLO

SCREW BEAN   Strombocarpa pubescens (Benth.) A. Gray
PEA FAMILY   Leguminosæ

The *tornillo,* or screw bean, received its English name—the equivalent of the Spanish one—from the character of its seed pods, which are spirally twisted and coiled, especially after they have dried and split.

The natural habitat of this plant is in the southern part of New Mexico and across the border into México, but evidently some animal or bird carried its seed up to the lava beds of La Bajada, just below Santa Fé, for one solitary tree of this species grows there, and with the assistance of its children springing around its base, hides for a brief interval the surrounding volcanic rock with feathery leafage.

When babies' eyes become inflamed during the summer, the green leaves are crushed, mixed with their mother's milk, and placed in a small cloth bag, which is pressed so the liquid is dropped into their *ojos negros.* Moreover, the leaves may be crushed and mixed with water to form a wash for sore eyes in persons of any age. In case inflammation of the stomach exists, the *tornillo* seeds are chewed and swallowed with water,

190

and if bladder trouble has arisen, a tea can be made from the leaves and drunk three times a day.

The trunks and branches form good fuel and fence posts, and the bean pods contain a large amount of sugar, which can be converted, by boiling, into a fair kind of molasses.

Tornillo has a very useful sister in the mesquite bush (Prosopis glandulosa Torr.), which is like the other except that the beans are somewhat larger and the pods do not curl. A medicinal tea is derived from its leaves, a gum from its bark, a nutritious food and sweet beverage from its ripe seed vessels, honey from its blossoms, fuel and building material from its sturdy wood.

The seeds ripen in bean-like pods which turn a pale golden shade in late summer, and which are fed to horses, burros, and cattle to fatten them after a lean and dry season. These pods are also pounded into meal by the Indians of the Southwestern deserts and made into cakes. These retain all their nutritious quality as long as they are kept perfectly dry, but let them be soaked in water so that fermentation sets in and the product is very similar to old English mead: fizzy and intoxicating.

The amber-colored gum which appears at the forked branches of the shrub is not unlike gum Arabic, and makes an excellent mucilage and a soothing gargle for the throat.

When the Spaniards invaded México, they evidently adapted the ancient Aztec name of *mizquitl* to their manner of expression, and changed it to *mesquit,* and also brought with them, as a heritage of the Moorish occupation of Spain, the word *algarroba* (English carrob), of Arabic origin, and applied it to the mesquit's bean pods. According to the early Spanish texts, the Aztec used a decoction of its leaves to restrain excessive mensis, and its bruised bark as an astringent.

But the Coahuila and Pima Indians made a makeshift sugar from its sweet pods. The Pima also took the sap internally as a cure for respiratory afflictions, and the Papago Indians drank a decoction of its powdered white inner bark as an intestinal antispasmodic.

TREMENTINA DE PIÑON

Trementina de piñon is the fresh white pitch that is extracted from the piñon tree (Pinus edulis) by incision.

Spanish New Mexicans mix the new *trementina* with *punche mexicano* (native tobacco) and salt, spread it over a piece of paper, and place the preparation on the temples to relieve headache. After piñon pitch has been exposed to the air, it gradually hardens, and may be ground into a fine powder often rubbed on rheumatic joints.

An ointment called *sanalotodo* (cure-all) also is made with this substance. It is said to have the amazing property of drawing out splinters, cactus thorns, tumors in the fingers, or pus from any wound. First a tablespoonful of *trementina* must be washed seven times in the tepid water, the water being changed with every washing. Then this must be melted with one teaspoonful of *manteca de pela* (the outside fat of sheep), and one-half square of *cera de campeche* (bee's wax), one-half inch of *cera de vela* (candle wax), and two ounces of *aceite de comer* (olive oil). These are all beaten together until they solidify, when the yolk of an egg is put in the mixture and the whipping is continued until the preparation becomes an ointment. Should the affliction have been a sliver, the old hard piñon gum must be chewed and placed on the wound after the splinter has been drawn out in order to heal the irritation completely.

An informant at Chimayo once told me that *trementina de piñon* had saved many people from operation for piles. A small amount of the resin was washed seven times in cold water, then heated in two tablespoons of lard and strained. To this was added the well-beaten whites of two eggs and two tablespoonsful of sulphur. The entire mixture then was thoroughly whipped and applied to the cleansed surface of the afflicted part.

TRIGO

WHEAT
GRASS FAMILY

Triticum æstivum L.
Gramineæ

Spanish New Mexicans boil wheat roots and wash their heads with the resultant tea, to promote the growth of the hair.

These descendants of the *conquistadores* still thresh their wheat according to the old methods of Biblical times. The freshly-cut grain is heaped into a mound on carefully-swept, circular, earthen threshing floors, and goats, horses, or sheep are driven around the pile until they have trodden the kernels from all the stalks. Isolated *rancheros* usually have their own threshing floors, but the people of tiny hamlets support a communal undertaking where all may thresh their grain. Wheat is separated from the chaff by winnowing, and it is almost as common a sight in the autumn to see someone holding aloft a container from which a stream of auburn grain is falling, as it is to come upon a group driving their stock around a stack of unthreshed wheat.

UÑA DE GATO

PATITOS
CAT CLAW
CAT'S CLAWS
BLACK LOCUST
PEA FAMILY

Acacia greggii A. Gray

Leguminosæ

This locuts defends itself with an abundant armory of extremely sharp spines, as piercing as those on any feline paw, hence its name, cat's claws, or *uña de gato*.

Spanish New Mexican children suck its flowers for their honey, just as children in other parts of the world delight in clover and honeysuckle blossoms because of the nectar they contain.

Of another acacia is written: "Acatia maketh the heare

blacke if it be washed and often wet in the water wherein it hath bene soked. The leaves and tender croppes of Acatia do setle and strengthen members out of joynte, if they be bathed or soaked in the hoate bath or stue made with the broth thereof". (Dodœns, "Historie of Plantes", London, 1578).

VARAS DE SAN JOSÉ
VARITAS DE SAN JOSÉ

BARAS DE SAN JOSÉ   Pentstemon torreyi Benth.
SCARLET BUGLER
RED PENTSTEMON
BEARD TONGUE
HUMMING-BIRD'S DINNER HORN
FIGWORT FAMILY   Scrophulariaceæ

We are indebted to the Figwort family for many of our most striking and handsome wild flowers, among them being the Indian paint brush, the gay collinsia, the useful bee plant, and the familiar owl's clover, all of which illumine our fields and woods with their brilliant patterns.

The *varas de San José* (staves of St. Joseph) is something of a dashing fellow too, holding himself proudly erect, and apparently particularly conscious of his bluish-green leaves with rippled edges, and his vivid scarlet blossoms that trumpet invitations to the hummingbirds to become constant attendants.

Zuñi Indians chew the root and rub it over their rabbit-sticks to insure success in the hunt. "A rabbit-stick thus treated", they affirm, "is sure to kill every rabbit at which it is aimed, provided the thrower has a good heart".

Spanish New Mexicans boil the flowering top of the *varas de San José* in water, strain the liquid, and drink it for kidney trouble and for a cold in the chest. The boiled dry or fresh flowers, with the addition of enough sugar to make a syrup, are given to babies with whooping-cough when they have

194

paroxysms. Infants under six months of age are treated with one-half teaspoonful, but those who are older take an entire teaspoonful.

In cases of excessive mensis, the whole plant is broken into small pieces, and boiled in water. The patient must drink three swallows of the decoction, and bathe the lower portions of the body with this liquid. This may be another indication of the Doctrine of Signatures in the utilization of plants.

YEDRA

HIEDRA   Rhus toxicodendron
POISON IVY
CASHEW FAMILY   Anacardiaceæ

The poison ivy, with its tri-lobate leaves, thrice-warns the unwary at the tip of every stem to beware its noxious venom, but the people of Río del Medio sometimes are called upon to treat those who have been affected by the poison. They accomplish this end by mixing a large quantity of salt with flour and applying it to the inflamed portions.

Although it is difficult to determine whether the Spanish or Arabic word formed the basis of the other, the Moors refer to a kind of ivy as *yidra*. This is the well-known English Ivy, Hedera helix L., and it is not native in North America. But whereas the New Mexican term is applied to poison ivy, the Arabic is used for a vine whose leaves, they affirm, if tied over an infection, will draw out the pus.

YERBABUENA

SPEARMINT   Mentha spicata L.
MINT FAMILY   Labiatæ

I introduce you to an old friend, the spearmint, whose aromatic odor and refreshing taste our ancestors knew so well, and which not only is used in food for its popular flavor by the Spanish New Mexicans, but also is prized highly by them

195

for its valuable carminative qualities. The mere mention of *yerbabuena* will bring a thrill to any Spanish-American; he will be enraptured, and little murmurs of delight will escape his lips. If he can hold a sprig to his nose, he is like a Frenchman in ecstasy over some rare vintage.

An excellent tea for indigestion can be made of the dry or green mint leaves, boiling water, cinnamon, cloves, and nutmeg, strained and taken hot. Rather palatable for "that dark brown taste"—the morning after! As a vermifuge, an infusion is prepared carefully outside the sickroom, and the patient must hold his nose very tightly while drinking the decoction, every morning, before a late breakfast. Also, wounds and sores are washed with the tea, and it is considered a very fine general remedy, often being taken for diarrhea and neuralgia. Before childbirth, a decoction of *yerbabuena,* with the addition of cinnamon, is drunk by expectant mothers.

Although it is impossible to determine the connection between the latter treatment in New Mexico and the prescription in the Maya texts advocating a decoction of mashed mint leaves and honey to bring on parturition, I was particularly pleased when I discovered this similarity of usage among the peoples of old and New Mexico.

YERBA DE ALONSO GARCÍA

Dalea formosa Torr.
(Parosela formosa (Torr.) Vail)
PEA FAMILY   Fabaceæ

A Spaniard, Cavanilles by name, anagramatically inclined, juggled the word Psoralea, the botanical term for one member of the Pea family, and achieved Parosela, one designation for the group in which *yerba de Alonso García* belongs. The valid generic name, however, is Dalea. A comparison of Psoralea and Dalea reveals a striking similarity. Both are sturdy shrubs with terminal clusters of tiny flowers, and both possess

196

small glands under their leaves from which springs the delightful aroma that has given pleasure to so many people.

Another Spaniard, Lieutenant-General Alonso García, whose reputed cruelty may have been a contributory cause to the Pueblo uprising in 1680, achieved partial atonement for his sins by leading the small band of colonial survivors who had escaped from the Indians out of their temporary encampment at Isleta, and into comparative safety at El Paso. And it may have been in gratitude for their deliverance that Spanish New Mexicans have given his name to the *Parosela formosa*.

The descendants of those early settlers make a bath from the plant for rheumatism, and while bathing, drink a cup of *yerba de Alonso García tea*. They also administer a similar treatment to their children if they suffer from rickets. In this connection I have been told that powdered *cuerno de venado* (deer horn) sometimes is mixed with the food of children who have rickets.

YERBA DE CORIZ

I am told that the leaves of an undetermined plant known as *yerba de coriz* are very fine, and that the roots, though slightly bitter to the taste, are sweet as sugar. It is to be found at Pedernal beyond Madrid by the Laguna Colorada.

Natividad Arquero of Cochiti affirms that for a long time he had a bad cough on the lung. He chewed, he says, a tiny bit of the root and disgorged a little worm which had caused the cough. As a result he was cured.

YERBA DE SAN PEDRO

The undetermined plant known as *yerba de San Pedro* may have been named for the Apostle who is represented so often bearing the keys to heaven and hell, because of its utility in driving away the purgatory of sores and restoring the afflicted to a haven of health.

The inflammations, or *golpes* as the Spanish New Mexicans call them, are washed with tepid water and sprinkled three or four times a day with one teaspoonful of the herb's dry ground leaves. This treatment is continued until the pus has been extracted.

All manner of aches and pains are counteracted by giving the patient a bath prepared from boiling the entire plant in water. Then the patient must be put to bed and made to sweat profusely.

YERBA DE LA GOLONDRINA

SPURGE   Euphorbia serpyllifolia Pers.
SPURGE FAMILY   Euphoribiaceæ

Yerba de la golondrina, the herb of the swallow, unlike its namesake is a bashful plant that hugs the ground. Since it bears staminate or pistillate flowers or exclusively either kind on one plant, it cannot effect fertilization of its seeds unassisted, and consequently depends largely on insects for this function.

This species of Euphorbia must not be confused with the California *yerba de la golondrina,* which is the Euphorbia maculata, and was formerly employed in the treatment of skin diseases, corneal opacities, and warts.

The species that occur in New Mexico have long enjoyed wide repute as a remedy against rattlesnake bites. The most common methods of counteracting the venom consisted in poulticing the plant on the wound, and drinking a decoction of the leaves.

For tonsilitis the crushed green leaves are made into a poultice, with the addition of a little salt, and placed on the throat. If it becomes necessary to employ this remedy during the winter, the dry leaves are moistened and used in the same way.

The fresh plant is rubbed on small itching pimples or rash, and a gargle is prepared from a decoction of the leaves.

198

The stems and roots of *yerba de la golondrina* contain a milky sap, latex that is considered excellent for warts, and as in the case of other plants having a lacteal juice, Spanish New Mexicans affirm that if goats and cows eat large quantities, they will produce more milk.

There is another, more involved, cure for warts that is resorted to by those of a more mystical turn of mind. A string is tied so tightly around a wart that a small section is removed. This is put in a cloth, tied up, and placed in the middle of the crossroads. If the bag is picked up by someone, he or she is said to acquire the wart, and the original sufferer is thereby released.

YERBA DE LA MALA MUJER

ASTER FAMILY

Brickellia reniformis A. Gray
Compositæ

The shrub called *yerba de la mala mujer,* literally the herb of the bad woman, occurs on La Bajada below Santa Fé, and is noticeable for the richness and sweetness of its perfume which is especially pleasant in the evenings.

The written instructions of a Pecos *médica*—to the letter—concerning "llerva de la mala mujer", were "for tootheack boilid and then tack some in your mought".

YERBA DE LA NEGRITA

MALLOW FAMILY

Sphæeralcea fendleri A. Gray
Malvaceæ

Yerba de la negrita, the herb of the little negress, is covered with a yellow pubescence and has slender branching stems, variously lobed leaves, and numerous axillary salmon flowers.

Spanish New Mexicans grind a handful of the fresh leaves and add a pint of warm water when tumors are to be treated. They strain the infusion and give it to the patient, a small

199

cupful every day for a week. "This loosens the tumor and it comes out", they affirm.

In order to counteract swellings which occur in the summer months, like those caused by mosquitoes and ants, the plant is crushed, salt is added, and the preparation is applied; and the mashed roots, mixed with a little flour to make them stick, are poulticed over broken bones.

A shampoo made from the mashed leaves and flowers is said to promote the growth of hair, and a plaster, prepared like that for insect bites, is placed on the forehead for headache.

YERBA DE LA PIEDRA
YERBA DE LA PEÑA

GREY LICHEN OR MOSS

Spanish New Mexicans rub grey lichens on the gums as a cure for pyorrhea, and grind and apply the plant for any kind of sore or injury *(lastimada)*.

An Indian *médico* of Santo Domingo pueblo informed me that this plant should be boiled green and given to one who talks and laughs to himself. A similar treatment was good for headaches, he affirmed.

There is another more popular treatment for headache which is not so dependent upon medicinal virtues. Whenever one sees a Spanish-American of known bibulous habits abroad on a Monday morning, a rare occurrence in itself, he is pretty sure to be wearing on each temple a bright blue stamp provided by a thoughtful Government with each cigarette package. What better use could be found for a tax receipt than a cure for a bad alcoholic headache?

200

YERBA DE LA QUINTANA

ASTER FAMILY

Aplopappus spinulosus DC.
Compositæ

This flower, whose vernacular name, when literally translated into English, means herb of the country mansion, is conspicuous for its large heads of yellow inflorescence.

For abcesses or swellings of the face and neck, the plant is mashed with a little salt by local *médicas* and put in the mouth where the pain exists.

YERBA DE LA SANGRE

SANGRE DE CRISTO
"OREGON GRAPE"
TRAILING MAHONIA
CREEPING BARBERRY
HOLLY-LEAFED BARBERRY
BARBERRY FAMILY

Mahonia repens
Berberis repens Lindl.

Berberidaceæ

The creeping barberry is a low prostrate shrub, unlike its more upstanding sister species, and has, with due regard for the magic of numbers, from three to seven leaflets which turn red in the autumn, and which are stiff and prickly, like holly. The stems and especially the roots contain a bright yellow substance (berberin) with a very bitter taste and good dyeing properties. I have not been able to find that the Spanish New Mexicans employ the dye.

They boil the leaves in water and drink the tea twice a day for anemia, and take the decoction early in the morning before eating to bring on menstruation. Since *yerba de la sangre* means herb of the blood, it may have been thus named because of that use, and later may have acquired its reputation as a blood purifier, or vice versa. The leaves or roots are boiled and drunk tepid to cleanse the blood.

A decoction of the leaves and branches is used by the Navajos in curing rheumatism.

At various times, Spanish Americans have made a tea from the roots as an alterative, anti-syphilitic, diuretic, and laxative.

201

YERBA DE LA TUSA

EMBARRAÑADA
CONE FLOWER
ASTER FAMILY

Lepachys tagetes A. Gray

Compositæ

Nearly everyone who comes to the "West" for the first time wants to see a prairie dog, and if he visits one of their towns in New Mexico, he is also likely to see the "herb of the prairie dog", or *yerba de la tusa,* a perennial weed with narrow alternate leaves and yellow to brownish-purple terminal heads.

Without any attempt to distinguish the disease, Spanish New Mexicans tell me, with charming inclusiveness, that for large red pustules all over the body, you should boil an armful of *yerba de la tusa* in enough water for a bath. The patient should bathe in the liquid, wrap himself up in a sheet, and go directly to bed. The following morning he will awake and discover that the angry spots have vanished! The same treatment is supposed to relieve rheumatism.

The finely-powdered root, placed upon an aching tooth, should reduce the throbbing.

YERBA DE LA VIRGEN

SCARLET GAURA
EVENING PRIMROSE FAMILY

Gaura coccinea Pursh
Onagraceæ

It is highly fitting that so delicate an herb should have been called after the Holy Mother.

The Greek word *gaura* means proud, and anyone who has seen this plant's slender, erect stems, vigorous oblong leaves, and mellow white and scarlet flowers, instantly realizes that it truly deserves its scientific name also.

For muscular rheumatism, the plants are ground or mashed (dry or green), and rubbed on the limbs.

202

YERBA DEL APACHE

WESTERN WALLFLOWER   Erysimum elatum Nutt.
WALLFLOWER
MUSTARD FAMILY   Cruciferæ

In Europe, the Erysimums often grow against old walls, hence their popular English name. *Yerba del apache* is a grayish plant with leaves closely resembling the stem, and with golden yellow petals singularly clawed. It possesses the peculiarity of having, as do the pepper grass and the shepherd's purse, six stamens; two of these are shorter than the others.

In order to relieve pneumonia, its roots are chewed by the Spanish New Mexicans, spat on the afflicted back, and rubbed in. This is done two or three times to alleviate the pain. The ground roots are mixed with whiskey and water to be bound on rheumatic limbs. The root powder also is blown into the throat for soreness.

Zuñi Indians, without discriminating between the different varieties of Erysimums, grind the entire plant, and mix it with a small quantity of water. The infusion is applied to the forehead and temples to counteract pain caused by exposure to heat, and as a preventive against sunburn.

YERBA DEL BUEY

PEGAPEGA (El Rito)   Grindelia aphanactis Rydb.
GUM PLANT
GUM WEED
RESIN WEED
AUGUST FLOWER
ASTER FAMILY   Compositæ

The large, solid yellow flower heads of the *yerba del buey,* or herb of the ox, which one might easily mistake for the inflorescence of golden eye, may be seen growing in profusion during August on the plains and hills throughout New Mexico. One should not allow the name *pegapega,* which sometimes is given this plant by reason of its gummy exudation of milky resin, to mislead him into any misconception of the *yerba del buey's* identification, or to ally it with another plant invariably called *pegapega,* elsewhere described.

When cross fertilization by normal means fails, the gum plant resorts to self-pollination. The inner anthers cast out their pollen, some of which must fall upon the outer stigmas, thus achieving seed production.

With a consistent regard for the potential influence of magical numbers, Spanish New Mexicans boil three times three *yerba del buey* buttons (buds or flowers) in three pints of water, until only one pint of liquid remains. This should be taken for kidney disorders by the wineglassful, three times a day. As it has a very bitter taste, a little *piloncillo* (Mexican brown sugar) often is added.

The herb also has a reputation for the easing of rheumatic pains when the fresh, green plants are crushed and applied.

During the winter, for *resfrio en los huesos,* "cold in the bones", the dried sprigs are thoroughly sprinkled with hot water and a quantity is piled on a heated adobe brick. The whole is wrapped in a cloth and held beside the aching parts. The steam emanating from this preparation effects the cure.

It is claimed that, for an ordinary cold, and in allaying stomach trouble, a tea is efficacious, and that in cases of paralysis, hot baths of this weed are particularly beneficial.

Yerba del buey not only is devoted to medicinal purposes, but is found useful in making brooms for the threshing floor, and children delight in teasing one another by sticking the resinous buds on their victims' faces.

There is a related species, Grindelia robusta Nutt., from which the drug Grindelia is derived. This is sold in our pharmacies and taken primarily for asthma, neuralgia, and bladder and kidney afflictions. Externally, it is applied in solution, particularly to blisters, burns, and to poison ivy and poison oak rash, and, in general, to all kinds of skin eruptions.

Nearly all its virtues were well known to the Indians of the Southwest.

YERBA DEL CABALLO

GROUNDSEL   Senecio filifolius Nutt.
ASTER FAMILY   Compositæ

No plant has a wider distribution in New Mexico than this. It blossoms nearly every month in the year in the southern part of the state, and is one of the first plants to bloom farther north.

To the Spanish-Americans of New Mexico, it is the *yerba del caballo,* the herb of the horse, but the English-speaking inhabitants have inherited an old Anglo-Saxon word that usually appears in two forms, *grundeswylige,* and *gundeswelge,* presumably a combination of *gund,* matter, and *swelgan,* to swallow, and gradually became modified until the modern term of "groundsel" was achieved.

The people of Cerro Gordo and Río del Medio seem to have incorporated part of the meaning of the old English word in one of their remedies, since they make a tea from this *yerba* and employ it as a gargle for sore throat.

At Chimayo, the allied Senecio multicapitatus Greenm. also is called *yerba del caballo,* and is crushed and rubbed on rheumatic limbs.

Among the Zuñi, the root of this variety is "ground to powder in the fraternity chamber, is mixed with cold water and the infusion rubbed over the limbs for 'aching bones'. This medicine is applied morning, noon, and night by the chosen theurgist, who must invoke the cougar of the north and the bear of the west during the application, as this medicine is the special property of these zooic gods".—(Matilda Coxe Stevenson, "Ethnobotany of the Zuñi Indians").

There is yet another *yerba del caballo,* Senecio ambroisiodes Rydb., which prefers the rugged slopes of high elevations, and which, when green, is rubbed upon rheumatic portions of the body until relief is obtained, or, when dry, the leaves are ground, slightly dampened, and used in the same manner by these Indians.

YERBA DEL CHIVATITO

YERBA DE ZORILLO CIMARRON   Chenopodium botrys L.
JERUSALEM OAK
GOOSEFOOT FAMILY   Chenopodiaceæ

This herb, like many of its kin, is a sticky plant, and quite disagreeably strong-scented. It was introduced from Europe long ago, and possesses deeply-toothed leaves, and extremely small greenish axillary flowers.

Spanish New Mexicans believe that it is effective in treating "cold in the stomach" when steeped in boiling water and taken internally. They also employ it to stop children from bed-wetting. This is done by soaking two small *yerba del chivatito* branches in four quarts of cold water until a wine color appears. The patient then is made to drink this liquid to the exclusion of all others until the remedy has accomplished its purpose.

YERBA DEL CHIVATO

Pericome caudata A. Gray

ASTER FAMILY   Compositæ

Ever since the association of men and animals, the former have woven about the latter a coexistence of spirit which has developed the varied forms of fetishism and shamanism, and man has relied on "bestiaries", witches' spells, healing balms, alluring scents, portentious entrails, necromancy, and black magic, derived from or based upon animality, in the determination of his actions, and in the treatment of his afflictions.

It is not inconsistent therefore, that many plants have been given vernacular names after familiar animals, such as the English cockscomb, dogwood, cranesbill, duckweed, and larkspur, to cite only a few. The New Mexican *yerba del chivato*, or the herb of the he-goat, is a Spanish example of the custom. In this instance, the vernacular name is in keeping with the strong goat-like odor which this plant exudes.

206

Local *médicas* prescribe a bath of the boiled roots of *yerba del chivato* for rheumatism, and advise the patient to go to bed immediately after bathing. They maintain that this treatment should be repeated eight times. Another method consists in rubbing the dry ground leaves of this *yerba* on rheumatic limbs.

YERBA DEL LOBO

ASTER FAMILY

Helenium hoopesii Gray
Compositæ

It is curious that several members of the Pea family begin with the letter "L"; loco weed, locust, lupine, licorice, and their cousin the *yerba del lobo,* herb of the wolf, are outstanding examples. The appearance of the *yerba del lobo,* herb of the wolf, is not so formidable as its namesake, although it is found in the higher altitudes that formerly were frequented by wolves. It possesses large leaves which arise in a spreading cluster directly from the root, not unlike the formation of the *yucca,* and like that plant also, it produces a tall flower stalk, with large yellow inflorescence at the top.

Wolves and witches and magic and "yarbs" long have been associated in popular beliefs, but I have found no evidence in New Mexico that indicates a coordination of thought between the powers supposedly attributed to wolves and the healing properties of the *yerba del lobo.* Spanish New Mexicans grind its dry roots and rub them on the afflicted parts for rheumatism or for pains in the ribs and shoulders caused by cold or penumonia. Such discomforts are also treated by applying a mixture of the pulverized root and whiskey *(mula),* or water, to the affected portions. It is believed that supposed cases of leprosy may be counteracted to good effect in a similar manner.

When stomach derangements arise, a *médica,* in the Jémez mountains advised me, the *yerba del lobo* roots should be chewed or boiled in water and the decoction drunk. It is very bitter if taken without sugar, but another informant insisted that it also made a good febrifuge when imbibed in this manner.

There is another variety of this plant, with purple flowers, which is found at Turquillo, which is considered excellent in that vicinity for *hincha del estomago,* infant's colic. A poultice is prepared by boiling in four cups of water a little *collálle* (Gutierreza tenuis Greene), cinnamon, cloves, nutmeg, *yerba del lobo* root, *oshà* (Ligusticum Porteri C. & R.), ginger and *altamisa de la sierra* (Artemisia franserioides Greene). When the resultant liquid has taken on a deep color, it is strained, and mixed hot with enough corn meal to make a paste. This is spread on the patient and covered with a cloth.

One instance was told to me of a child who had suffered from diarrhea for a month and was treated twice with this application. After the first time, the child asked for nourishment.

YERBA DEL NEGRO

GLOBE MALLOW   Sphæralcea cuspidata A. Gray
MALLOW FAMILY   Malvaceæ

Both the English and botanical names for *yerba del negro* are derived from the combination of two Greek words, *spaira,* meaning ball, and *alkea,* mallow.

It possesses numerous small axillary purple-red flowers, and unlike its dusky relative, *yerba de la negrita* (S. fendleri), its oblong leaves are not lobed.

At Tularosa, New Mexico, a midwife told me you must boil a small piece of the root in a glass of water to obtain a purge. This must be taken three times a day or before breakfast whenever necessary.

If a decoction of the plant is drunk every morning for nine days, it is supposed to act as a diuretic.

208

YERBA DEL OSO

COW PARSNIP   Heracleum lanatum Michx.
PARSLEY FAMILY   Umbelliferæ

Yerba del oso (bear weed) is a stout woolly herb, as both its local Spanish and botanical names imply, with large compound leaves and large white flowers. It grows along streams, and roots in bogs and swampy ground.

Spanish New Mexicans grind the root, place it in a paper tube, and spray diphtheritic throats. They prepare a gargle with one-half teaspoonful of the powdered root and a glass of water.

The root powder often is rubbed on the gums when teeth are loose, and applied to the entire body in order to reduce fever.

Paralytic patients are bathed three times a week in a solution of the plant.

For rheumatic pains and tremors in the heart, the roots are ground, mixed with lard and rubbed on, or the powder may be applied alone. Another method consists in boiling the roots and bathing the afflicted parts.

Spanish Californians call Rhamnus californica by the name, *yerba del oso,* and employ it against the distasteful effects of poison oak. A number of the branches are boiled in a tub of water, in which the patient bathes, rubbing the inflamed portions with the cooked branches as though with a cloth. It is maintained that this will bring quick relief.

YERBA DEL PECO

BANEBERRY   Actaea arguta Nutt.
COHOSH
CROWFOOT FAMILY   Ranunculaceæ

As nearly everyone knows, the familiar baneberry, with
yellow flowers, branched stems, and large leaves, grows in
soggy ground; consequently it frequents New Mexican swamps
and the banks of *acequias* in order to obtain the necessary
amount of moisture.

There appears to be some doubt as to the origin of its local
Spanish name. It is the contention of one group that the pseudonym of *yerba del peco* arose from its existence along the
Pecos river, or that it was called after the group of Indians
of that name, but further research has revealed that the Aztec
referred to a kind of Sonchus (sow-thistle) that grew in the
damp portions of western México as *peço*.

Although the roots and leaves of this *yerba* are poisonous
if taken internally, Spanish New Mexicans grind the former,
mix them with the powdered leaves of *punche* (native tobacco), and rub them, dry, on rheumatic limbs. I recently
learned that an entire family was severly poisoned when they
ate its roots, having mistaken them for *camote*.

When ripe, baneberry seeds are roasted and pulverized,
a pinch is put with a soft-boiled egg, and the entire preparation is eaten for diarrhea, vomiting, and tenesmus *(pujos)*.
Moreover, the Spanish New Mexicans believe that neuralgia,
which they refer to as "air in the head", may be counteracted
effectively by mixing the ground seeds with *piñon* pitch *(trementina)* and making the whole into plasters to be placed in
front of and behind the ear.

There is another plant, of striking and graceful appearance,
which grows near shady mountain streams, and which also is
called *yerba del peco*. It is the Cicuta occidentalis Greene, a
member of the Parsley family, known to the English-speaking
people as water hemlock or cowbane.

210

YERBA DEL PESCADO

Ever since Christ, calling the fishermen Peter and Andrew, said unto them: "Follow me, and I will make you fishers of men", fish have become symbols of the most sacred significance and mystical import during the progress and interpretation of Christianity. The fish was even a symbol of Christ in primitive and medieval Christian art. The origin is to be found in the initial letters of His names and titles in Greek, which together spell the word for fish. It was said to be represented in the oval-shaped figure pointed at both ends, and formed by the intersection of two circles, also knows as the *visica piscis*, which is common in ecclesiastical seals, and as an aureole in paintings surrounding figures of the Trinity.

Whether it was the presence of well-stocked streams, or the influence of this medieval significance that led to the use of the local name, *yerba del pescado,* the herb of the fish, probably never will be determined, but for our purposes it suffices that this plant is one of the most highly-prized herbs in New Mexico.

It grows in mountain meadows, and may be distinguished by its small fuzzy white flowers and double-shaded leaves, dark green on top, white underneath, which twist with the wind and catch the eye by their reflection of the sun when their white sides are exposed.

Its round root is ground and held in the mouth for any soreness and for halitosis. Pyorrhea is treated with a mouthwash made from the powdered roots, and when a Spanish New Mexican suffers from toothache, a small piece of damp cotton is sprinkled with the powder and placed in the cavity. The pulverized root also may be blown into the throat for adenoids.

Wounds and abrasions of the skin are supposed to heal more rapidly when finely-ground leaves of *yerba del pescado,* and *yerba de San Pedro,* are mixed and sprinkled on the injury.

YERBA DEL PUJO

This undetermined plant is supposed to look like *camote*. Its fine leaves grow close to the ground, and the white flowers tower above them.

Yerba del pujo evidently has had some part in determining its own name, since the Spanish New Mexicans boil a handful of it in a pint of water as a remedy against tenesmus, which they call *pujos*. The liquid is strained and drunk as often as required.

YERBA DEL SAPO

Franseria tenuifolia Gray
(Locally referred to as the male variety)
Franseria acanthicarpa Hook.
(Locally referred to as the female variety, and called Rosetilla at Chimayo)

ASTER FAMILY   Compositæ

Yerba del sapo, the herb of the toad, appears very early in the spring, like its namesake, and soon forms clumps of fine leaves close to the ground. Both varieties are covered with rather stiff hairs, but the tenuifolia, which grows much taller than the acanthicarpa, has less ovate leaves than the latter. Neither should be confsued with the *yerba del sapo* of California (Eryngium amethystinum), which formerly was employed as a diaphoretic and emmenagogue.

The Zuñi Indians administer a decoction of Franseria acanthicarpa for obstructed menstruation, and massage the abdomen with the same preparation immediately thereafter. They also place the ground root in a hollow tooth to relieve toothache.

When the burros bring heavy loads of firewood down from the mountains every autumn, their backs often are lacerated by the constant rubbing of their burdens, and, to speed the cure, their drivers sprinkle the dry powdered leaves of Franseria acanthicarpa over the sores.

There are a number of plants to which the Spanish New Mexicans have attributed two genders. In the group of alleged "bisexuals" belongs the *yerba del sapo* of which Franseria tenuifolia is the *macho,* or male; and Franseria acanthicarpa is the *hembra,* or female. As any *médica* can tell you, such a division is absolutely necessary, since it is essential, in effecting a cure with these particular varieties, that the man partake of the female herb, and that the woman employ the herb of the opposite sex.

In accordance with this belief, if a man has inflammation of the stomach, he must grind the green or dry leaves of the female *yerba del sapo,* and mix them with a pinch of salt and a small quantity of asparagus berries. Then he must steep them in a cup of hot or cold water, strain the liquid and drink it. And if a woman has ulcers of the stomach, she must mash thoroughly two handsful of male *yerba del sapo,* thus extracting the juice, add a little water, and drink three doses a day.

But if, by chance, she contracts *saltido,* a "jumping stomach", she should make a large ball of the green male plant, wrap it in cloth, and place it on the navel to stop the throbbing pulse. Naturally, a man with the same complaint must adopt a similar treatment, using the female *yerba* as his remedy.

YERBA DEL VASO

Yerba del vaso, meaning the herb of an artery or vein, a glass or vase, is employed in the treatment of stomach ailments.

At Vallecito de los Indios, the leaves of this undertemined herb are chewed, or if the stomach feel too full, a round ball of the plant is made and bound on the abdomen. A tea brewed from the entire herb often accompanies the latter remedy.

YERBA DEL ZORILLO

GOOSEFOOT FAMILY

Chenopodium incisum Poir.
Chenopodiaceæ

Yerba del zorillo, the herb of the skunk, is a retiring plant, seldom growing more than one foot high, but in the autumn it turns scarlet, and bears tiny bright red seeds.

This crimson fruit is boiled in water until it turns a wine color, then it is strained and given to babies for colic. A small handful of the plant, dry or fresh, often is boiled in a quart of water and administered to ease menstrual pains. A small glassful is drunk when necessary, and the patient is kept in bed.

Spanish New Mexicans firmly believe that, if the plants are soaked in water and a rheumatic patient bathes in the solution, it will bring relief.

YERBA FRIA

ASTER FAMILY

Sanvitalia aberti A. Gray
Compositæ

The *yerba fria* is a branched, low-growing plant with opposite leaves and greenish-yellow flowers. Formerly it was quite abundant, but now is comparatively scarce. The Spanish New Mexicans enjoy chewing the flower-head because it makes the saliva flow and produces a pleasant cool sensation in the mouth—hence its name of *yerba fria,* cold herb. Doubtless for the same reason it is used as a refrigerant.

A decoction of its leaves is supposed to be good for stomach trouble of all kinds.

When the teeth become stained, the flowers are chewed.

YERBA MANSA
YERBA DEL MANSO

YERBA MANSA   Anemopsis californica Hook & Arn.
YERBA DEL MANSO
LIZARD'S-TAIL FAMILY   Saururaceæ

Yerba del manso, which, according to Charles Francis Saunders, means the herb of the tamed Indian, is a low-growing perennial whose smooth light green leaves with reddish stems crowd the marshes, and whose large cream-white flowers, to adopt a Tennysonian phrase, sow the ground with stars.

It is common in wet, alkaline seeps throughout most of our Southwest, and probably, among all of the Spanish-Americans in the region, no other plant enjoys so wide a medicinal fame as *yerba mansa,* or has a higher repute. Both Spanish Californians and Spanish New Mexicans emphatically declare that its creeping aromatic root is applied with excellent results —whether made into a tea, powder, or a poultice—to all manner of abrasions, burns, and sores in men and animals.

In New Mexico, natives gargle inflamed throats with a teaspoonful of the dry ground root and one-half glass of water, and place the crushed root on ulcerated gums. They also mix powdered *punche Mexicano* (native tobacco), a small piece of chewing tobacco, a bit of old sole leather that had been heated in a fire until it had become red and then was cooled and ground, and about an inch of pulverized *yerba del manso* root, as an ointment for piles. All of these substances must be beaten together and finally mixed with some beef drippings. This amount should produce enough salve for nine days.

Those of Spanish origin in California consider that an application of wilted *yerba mansa* leaves will reduce swellings, and that the entire plant, in the form of a wash or poultice, can be used with good results for rheumatism.

The Spanish people of both California and New Mexico

215

take a decoction of the herb as a blood purifier, and in the treatment of derangements of the mucuous membrane and for digestive upsets. Spanish American adults in New Mexico stir a teaspoonful of the powdered root into a glass of water and drink the whole three times a day to counteract simple dysentery.

For bleeding dysentery an egg is boiled slightly in the early morning, without allowing the white to harden; the tip of the shell is removed, and a small quantity of the ground root is poured in. This preparation is immediately drunk from the shell.

Children who suffer from stomach trouble and babies affected by colic are given relief in a slightly different manner. The roots are boiled in water until a red liquid develops. This is imbibed at intervals until relief is secured.

The Maricopa and Pima Indians long have taken a decoction of the plant as an antiluetic. One writer affirms that this remedy "is known to be effective".

YERBA SIN RAIZ
YERBA MALA

CUSCUTA   Cuscuta curta Engelmann
CÚSCUTA
STRANGLE WEED
LOVE-VINE
DODDER
GOLDEN-THREAD
MORNING GLORY FAMILY   Convolvulaceæ

"Doder is a strange herbe, without leaves, and without roote, lyke unto a thread, much snarled and wrapped togither, confusely winding it self about hedges and bushes, and other herbs. The threads be sometimes red, sometimes white, upon the said threads are fastened, here and there little round heades or knoppes, bringing foorth at the first, small white flowers, and afterwarde a little seede."—(Dodœns).

216

This twining, leafless parasite with hollow threadlike stems, though popularly known as love-vine because of its clinging habits, little deserves so pleasant a name, as it quickly attaches itself to any nearby plant, and promptly sucks its nutriment. But in Florida we found another explanation of this name: a bunch of the love-vine often is gathered and thrown on the ground by a young man. If it lives, it is a true indication that his sweetheart loves the thrower, but if it dies, all is lost.

As there are four species in New Mexico, all having characteristics that appear the same to its Red and White inhabitants, only one name is applied to them all. However, I have found that Cuscuta comes from the Arabic, *Kushkut,* and Dodder from the Frisian *dodd,* a bunch, and the Dutch *dot,* ravelled thread. The Maya called it *X-Kan-le-cay,* a little yellow fish snare, so named because it resembles the nets with which they caught fish. Their texts prescribe a decoction of the plant for a bath to cure phthisis, and an infusion in the same manner for fever, biliousness, or jaundice. It is an old belief that the drug should harmonize with the malady, and certain colors were particularly efficacious for medicines, red and yellow the favorites, hence in the Maya prescription of a yellow plant for jaundice we see further proof of this faith.

At Santo Domingo pueblo, *yerba sin raiz,* herb without root, is used to reduce the swelling from insect bites, particularly those of a spider. It is gathered in summer, dried, boiled, and the decoction drunk. Or the sufferer, holding a cloth over his head to retain all the smoke, burns the plant with old dry *palmilla* (yucca flower stalk), to fumigate the bites, and decrease the irritations they have produced.

ZARZA
ZARZAPARILLA

WILD HOPS   Humulus lupulus neomexicanus Nels. & Ckll.
HEMP FAMILY   Cannabinaceæ

Here is another example of the indiscriminate use of the word *zarza* by the Spanish-speaking people in New Mexico, to indicate a vine. The term is a derivation of the Arabic *xaraç*, meaning a rose-like shrub, and even at present in Spain, *zarza* is the term given to a bramble in general and to the blackberry bush in particular. Although it is impossible to determine how New Mexicans came to designate creeping vines by *zarza,* it seems fairly probable that they have done so through the abandonment of the latter part of the other more uncommon word they apply to vines, *zarzaparilla*. *Zarzaparilla* is a combination of the true Spanish *zarza* and *parra*—the latter meaning grapevine.

The eighteenth century Castilian for hops was *lúpudos,* now spelled *lupulos,* and was developed from the same root as the two English words lupulin and lupulite. Lupulin is the yellow powder procured by beating or rubbing the strobiles, and then sifting out the grains which form about one-seventh part of the hops. Lupulite is the bitter principle of hops.

Wild hops in appearance look exactly like the cultivated variety, having the familiar bunched white flowers, lobed leaves, and hanging pale-colored cones.

These cones, in olden times, were taken internally as a decoction, since they were supposed to exert a powerful sedative and hypnotic action without the bodily disorders caused by opium, and an ancient custom, formerly widely practiced, was to sleep on a pillow stuffed with hops as a means of obtaining sleep.

New Mexican *señoras* often use the wild variety in raising their bread, and drink a tea brewed from the plant as a remedy for the blood. If one of their family should suffer from swollen

218

limbs as a result of dropsy, two handsful of the hops flowers are put in a tub of boiling water, and the patient is bathed in the solution, after which he must go to bed immediately and be made to sweat profusely. A similar treatment is administered for paralysis. But in curing rheumatism, the bathing solution is prepared from the roots of hops, from the roots of *coronillo* (blanket flower), and *yerba del caballo* (Senecio filifolius Nutt.)

ZARZILLA

ASTER FAMILY

Erigeron flagellaris A. Gray
Compositæ

Zarzilla is a fine, spreading herb of an ash color, with slender, whip-like stems. The people of Río del Medio make a tea from the plant for kidney trouble.

THE HERBS
THE PEOPLE
THE PLACE

•

Miguel Lamy and Wife 1

2

Lirios decorating Penitente graves

3

Calabazilla

4

Pinhué

Tomatito

Hongos

Yerba de la Golondrina

8

Flor de Santa Rita

9

Oshá

10

Barbasco

Oshá

12

Malvas

Tomate del Campo

Orégano de la Sierra   **14**

Alma Sauco   **16**

Flor de San Juan   18

Dormilón

Cebadilla

Yerba del Caballo

Yerba de la Sangre 24

Lechones   **26**

Pegapega

28

Amole, Yucca Barcata

BIBLIOGRAPHY

●

ARMSTRONG, Margaret

Field Book of Western Wild Flowers. In collaboration with J. J. Thornber. Putnam, New York. 1915.

ARIAS-CARVAJAL, Pio

Plantas que Curan y Plantas que Matan. Casa Editorial Maucci, Barcelona. 1903.

AUSTIN, MARY

The Land of Little Rain. Houghton, Mifflin, Boston. 1903.

BARD, Cephas L.

Medicine and Surgery Among the First Californians. Touring Topics, Los Angeles. Jan. 1930.

BARNES, Nellie

American Indian Love Lyrics. Macmillan, New York. 1925.

BEVERLY, Robert

History and Present State of Virginia. London. 1705.

BOTKIN, B. A.

Folk-say, a Regional Miscellany. Oklahoma Folk Lore Society, 1929-1930.

BROWN, Brian

Wisdom of the Chinese, Their Philosophy in Sayings and Proverbs. Preface by Ly Hoi Sang. Brentano, New York. 1920.

253

BROWN, Stewardson — *Alpine Flora of the Canadian Rocky Mountains.* Putnam, New York. 1907.

BUREAU OF AMERICAN ETHNOLOGY — *Annual Report.* 1883-84. 1887. 1890-91. 1891-92. 1894. 1896. Government Printing Office, Washington.

BURKE, John G. — *Folkfoods of the Rio Grande Valley and Northern Mexico.* Journal of American Folklore. Vol. VIII, No. XXVIII. January-March. 1895.

CAIN, Stanley — *The Doctrine of Signatures.* Science News Letter. Vol. 16, No. 8. 1947

CHANDLER, Katherine — *Habits of California Plants.* Educational Publ. Co., San Francisco. 1903.

CLEMENTS, Frederic E. and CLEMENTS, Edith S. — *Rocky Mountain Flowers.* ed. 3. H. W. Wilson & Co., New York. 1928.

COULTER, John M. and NELSON, Aven — *New Manual of Botany of the Central Rocky Mountains.* American Book Co., New York. 1909.

DARWIN, Charles — *Movements of Plants.* Appleton, New York. 1876.

CULPEPER, Nicholas — *Complete Herbal.* David McKay Co., Philadelphia [n.d.]

DAVIS, W. W. H. — *El Gringo, New Mexico and Her People.* Harpers, New York. 1857.

DEPARTMENT OF BIOLOGICAL STUDIES, DEPARTMENT OF AGRICULTURE, MEXICO — *Catalogo Alfabetico de Nombres Vulgares y Cientificos de Plantas que Existen en México.* Distrito Federal, Mexico. 1923.

DODOENS, REMBERT — *A Niewe Herball or Historie of Plantes.* London. 1578.

FERGUSSON, Erna — *Dancing Gods.* Alfred A. Knopf, New York. 1931.

FIROR, Ruth A. — *Folkways in Thomas Hardy.* Univ. of Pennsylvania Press, Philadelphia. 1931.

254

Fox, Helen Morgenthau   *Gardening with Herbs for Flavor and Fragrance.* Macmillan, New York. 1933.

Guthe, Carl E.   *Pueblo Pottery Making, a study at the village of San Ildefonso.* Paper no. 2 of the Southwestern Expedition. Yale Univ. Press, New Haven. 1925.

Harrington, M. R.   *The Cat-tail Eater.* Masterkey. Southwest Museum, Los Angeles. 1938.

Hernandes, Francisci and Reccho, Nardo Antonió   *Rerum Medicarum Novae Hispaniae Thesaurus Sev Plantarum Animaluim Mineralium Mexicanorum.* Vitalis Mascardi, Rome. 1651.

Higgins, Ethel Bailey   *Our Native Cacti.* A. T. de la Mare Co., New York. 1931.

Holling, Clancy   *New Mexico Made Easy.* Rockwell F. Clancy Co., Chicago. 1923.

Holmes, Oliver Wendell   *Medical Essays.* Houghton, Mifflin, Boston. 1904.

Hough, Walter   *Hopi Snake Dance.* Passenger Department, Santa Fe RR., 1901.

Jones, Paul A.   *Coronado and Quivira.* Lyons, Kansas. 1937.

Housekeeper's Manual. Nashville, Tenn. Jan. 1, 1875.

Laughlin, Ruth   *Caballeros.* Caxton. Caldwell, Idaho 1945.

Leyel, C. F. (Mrs.)   *Magic of Herbs.* Harcourt Brace, New York. 1926.

Longyear, Burton O.   *Trees and Shrubs of the Rocky Mountain Region.* Putnam, New York. 1927.

Los Angeles County Medical Association   *Bulletin.* June 19, 1930.

Lumholtz, Carl   *New Trails in Mexico.* Scribners, New York. 1912.

Masterkey. Vol. 7. Southwest Museum, Los Angeles. Sept., 1933.

255

MATHEWS, F. Schuyler	*Field Book of American Wild Flowers.* Putnam, New York. 1905.
MERRIAM, C. Hart	*Dawn of the World, Weird Tales of Mewan Indians.* Arthur H. Clark, Cleveland. 1910.
MEYER, Joseph E.	*Herbalist and Herb Doctor.* Indiana Herb Gardens, Hammond, Ind. 1918.
MINSHEU, John	*Guide Into the Tongues, with Their Agreement and Consent, One with Another, as Also Their Etymologies, That is, the Reasons and Dirivations* [sic] *of All or Most Part of Words, in These Nine Languages.* ed. 2. John Haviland, London. 1627.
MONARDES, Nicholas	*Joyfull Newes Out of the New-Found World Wherein Are Declared, the Rare and Singular Vertues of Diuers Herbs, Trees, Plantes, Oyles & Stones.* London. 1596.
NAIDU, Sarojini	*Broken Wing: Songs of Love, Death and Destiny.* John Lane Co., New York. 1917.
PARSONS, Mary Elizabeth	*Wild Flowers of California, Their Names, Haunts, and Habits.* Payot, Upham & Co., San Francisco. 1900.
POWERS, Stephen	*The Tribes of California.* Dept. of the Interior, U. S. Geographical and Geological Survey. Government Printing Office, Washington. 1877.
ROBBINS, Wilfred William, PEABODY, John Harrington; and FRIERE-MARRECO, Barbara.	*Ethnobotany of the Tewa Indians.* Bureau of Am. Ethnology Bull. 55. Government Printing Office, Washington. 1916.
ROYS, Ralph L.	*Ethno-botany of the Maya.* Tulane Univ., Middle American Research ser., publ. no. 2. New Orleans, 1931.
SAGARD-THEODAT, Gabriel	*History of Canada.* 1636.

256

SAFFORD, William E.   *Daturas of the Old World and New.* Smithsonian Inst. Rep. 1920. Government Printing Office, Washington. 1922.

SAUNDERS, Charles Francis   *Useful Wild Plants of the United States and Canada.* Robert M. McBride & Co., New York . 1926.

SAUNDERS, Charles Francis   *Western Wild Flowers and Their Stories.* Doubleday, Doran & Co., New York. 1933.

SEDGWICK, Mabel Cabot; and CAMERON, Robert   *Garden Month by Month.* Frederick A. Stokes Co., New York. 1907.

SHAKESPEARE, William   *Complete Works.* Walter J. Black, New York. 1925.

SMITH, Walter R.   *Animals and Plants in Oklahoma Folk-Cures.* Folk-say. 1929.

STANDLEY, Paul C.   *Some Useful Native Plants of New Mexico.* Smithsonian Inst. Rep. 1911: 447-462. Government Printing Office, Washington. 1912.

STEVENSON, Matilda Coxe   *Ethnobotany of the Zuñi Indians.* 30th Ann. Rep. Bureau American Ethnol. Government Printing Office, Washington. 1915.

STONE, Eric   *Clio Medica no. VII. Medicine Among the American Indians.* Paul B. Hoever, New York. 1932.

TWITCHELL, Ralph Emerson   *Old Santa Fe.* Santa Fe New Mexican Publ. Corp., Santa Fe. 1925.

WESTERMARCK, Edward   *Wit and Wisdom of Morocco.* Horace Liveright, New York. 1931.

     Westways. Automobile Club of Southern California, Los Angeles. January, 1934.

WOODWARD, F. L.   *Some Sayings of the Buddha, According to the Pali Canon.* Oxford Univ. Press, Madras. 1925.

WOOTON, E. O. and STANDLEY, Paul C.   *Flora of New Mexico.* Contrib. U.S. Nat. Herbarium, vol. 19. Government Printing Office, Washington. 1915.

257

INDEX

●

259

260

261

CHAN, *Salvia reflexa,* 59
(also Oshá, 141)
Chandelier cactus, Entraña, 79
Chapetes, see Hongos, 100
Charms, see Ajo, Albaca, Palo ama-
rillo, Plumajillo, Sangre de venado
Cheese, see Queso, 169
Chenopodiaceae, see Chamiso, Pazote,
Quelite salado, Yerba del chivatito,
Yerba del zorillo
Chenopodium album, Quelite salado,
168
Chenopodium ambrosioides, Pazote,
150
Chenopodium botrys, Yerba del chiva-
tito, 206
Chenopodium incisum, Yerba del zo-
rillo, 214
Cherry stone, Hueso de cereza, 103
Chester lily, Cebollita del campo, 55
CHICO, *Lycium pallidum,* 59
Chico bush, Chico, 59
CHICÓRIA, *Taraxacum officinale,* 60
Chicoriaceae, see Chicoria, Chicote em-
barrañada
Chicory family, see Chicoriaceae
CHICOTE EMBARRAÑADA, *Ly-
godesmia juncea,* 61
Childrens' games, see Calabazilla, Chi-
cória, Chicote embarrañada, Dor-
milón, Flor de Santa Rita, Guaco,
Hueso de cereza, Yerba del buey
CHILE, *Capsicum* sp., 62
(also see Culantro 13; Quelite sal-
ado 168; Orégano 138; Teques-
quite 182
CHILE PUERCO, *Amaranthus bli-
toides* 65
Chilicayote, Calabazilla, 45
Chili-Cojote, Calabazilla, 45
Chilicote, Calabazilla, 45
Chilicoyote, Calabazilla, 45
Chilli, Chile, 62
CHIMAJÁ, Aulospermum purpureum,
65
Chipped wood, Brazíl, 41
Chippewa Indians, Patita de leon, 148
Chiquete de embarrañada, Chicote em-
barrañada, 61
Chocoyole, Socoyol, 180
Choke cherry, Capulín, 51
Cholla, Entraña, 79
Choya, Entraña, 79
Chrysanthemum, Crisanta, 70
Chrysanthemum balsamita, Romero de
castilla, 172
Chrysanthemum Parthenium, Altamisa
mexicana, 31
Chrysanthemus graveolens, Chamiso
blanco, 57
Chuchupate, Oshá, 139

Cicuta occidentalis, Yerba del Peco,
210
CILANTRO, (see Culantro) *Corian-
drum sativum*
Cinnamon, use of, see Alegría, Añil
del muerto, Sangre de venado,
Yerbabuena, Yerba del lobo
Cirsium undulatum, Cardo santo, 53
Clastico de moscas, see Clavelina
CLAVELINA, *Saponaria officinalis,*
66
CLAVELLINA, Saporaria officinalis,
66
Cleome serrulata, Guaco, 93
Clocks, Alfilerillo, 27
Cloves, use of, see Alegría, Añil del
muerto, Guaco, Popotón, Yerba-
buena, Yerba del lobo
Cluster lily, Cebollita del campo, 55
Coahuilla Indians, see Lemita, Tor-
nillo
Cochiti Indians, see Oshá, Yerba de
coriz
Cocklebur, Cadillos, 42
Coentro, Culantro, 73
Cohosh, Yerba del peco, 210
Coliander, Culantro, 73
COLITA DE RATA, *Eriogonum
racemosum,* 67
COLITA DE RATÓN, *Eriogonum
racemosum,* 67
COLLÁLLE, *Gutierrezia tenuis,* 80
(also Oshá, 139; Yerba del lobo,
207)
Colorado rubber plant, Pinhué, 154
Colt's tail, Pazotillo, 151
Common cedar, Cuipa de sabina, 72
Common plantain, Lantén, 106
Compositae, see Aster family
Condalia spathulata, Teconblate, 181
Cone flower, Dormilón, 75; Yerba de
la tusa, 202
Consuelda, Chicória, 60
CONTRAYERBA, *Kallstroemia bra-
chystylis,* 67
(also Oshá, 139; Patito del país,
149)
Convovulác, Yerba sin raiz, 216
Copalquin, see Contrayerba, 67
Copper sulphate, see Piedra azul, 153
CORALILLO, *Arctostaphylos uva-
ursi,* 68
Coriander, Culantro, 73
Coriandro, Culantro, 73
Coriandrum sativum, Culantro, 73
CORONILLA, *Gaillardia pinnatifida,*
69
(Also Zarza, 218)
Cosmos, Amores, 32
Cosmos parviflorus, Amores, 32
COTA, *Thelesperma gracile,* 70
(also Manzanilla, 123-125)

263

265

266

267

PLUMAJILLO, *Achillea lanulosa,* 158
Poaceae, see Popotón, Roseta, Sacatito de ratón, Trigo, Yerba de la hormiga, Yerba del burro
Poison Ivy, Yedra, 195
Polemoniaceae, see Rosita morada, 175
POLÉO, *Mentha,* sp., 159
POLÉO CHINO, *Hedeoma oblongifolia,* 160
POLÉO DEL PAIS, *Mentha canadensis,* 161
(also Oshá, 139)
POLÉO GRANDE, *Mentha canadensis,* 161
Poliadas, see Cal, 43
Polygonaceae, see Caña agria, Colita de ratón, Lengue de vaca
PÓÑIL, *Fallugia paradoxa,* 161
(also see Maravilla, 125)
PONSO, *Tanacetum vulgare,* 163
POPOTÓN, *Stipa vaseyi,* 163
Popotillo, Cañutillo del campo, 49
Poppy family, see Papaveraceae
Populus angustifolia, Álamo sauco, 21
Populus wislizeni, Álamo de hoja redonda, 19
Porcupine grass, Popotón, 163
Posole, see Maíz, 116
Potatoes, Papas, 148
Prickly pear, Nopal, 133
Pride weed, Pazotillo, 151
Princess feather, Alegría, 24
Prunus Armeniaca, Albaricoque, 23
Prunus cerasus, Hueso de Cereza, 103
Prunus melanocarpa, Capulin, 51
Prunus persica, Durazno, 76
Puh, see Aguapá, 16
Pujos, Yerba del peco, 210
Pumpkin, Calabaza mexicana, 45
PUNCHE, *Nicotiana attenuata,* 165
(also see Maravilla, 125; Mata, 130; Póñil, 161; Trementina de piñon, 192; Yerba mansa, 215; Yerba del peco, 210)
PUNCHÓN, *Verbascum thapsus,* 166
Purple medic, Alfalfa, 26
Purplish red dye, see Capulín, Malva, Rosita morada

Quaker bonnets, Garbancillo, 91
Quamoclidion multiflorum, Maravilla, 125
QUELITE SALADO, *Chenopodium album,* 168
QUELITES COLORADO YUS, *Amaranthus powellii,* 169
QUELITES SALADOS, *Chenopodium album,* 168

QUELITES YUS, *Amaranthus powellii,* 169
Quercus fendleri, Encinillo, 78
Quercus gambelii, Encino, 78
QUESO (Cheese), 169

Rabbit brush, Chamiso cimmaron, 57
Rabbit thorn, Chico, 59
Rabbit's milk, Leche de conejo, 108
Radicula nasturtium-aquaticum, Berro, 40
Ragweed family ,see Ambrosiaceae
Raisin, use of, see Malva, Malva de castilla
RAMA DE SABINA, *Juniperus monosperma,* 169
Ranunculaceae, see Rude de la sierra, Yerba del peco, 177
Rattlesnake master, Escoba de la víbora, 80
Rattlesnake oil, Aceite de la vibora, 15
Rattlesnake root, Escoba de la víbora, 80
Rattlesnake weed, Escoba de la víbora, 80
Rattleweed, Frijolillo, 90
Red ants, Hormigas coloradas, 101
Red bearberry, Coralillo, 68
Red cockscomb, Alegría, 24
Red dye, see Alegría, Brazíl, Capulín, Cota, Palo duro, Rama de sabina, Rosita morada
Red pentstamon, Varas de San José, 194
Red-stemmed filaree, Alfilerillo, 27
REMOLINO, 170
(also Añis, 36)
Rennet, see Suajo, 71
Resfrio en los huesos, see Yerba del buey, 203
Resin weed, Yerba del buey, 203
Rhamnaceae, see Teconblate, 181
Rhus trilobata, Lemita, 112
Rhus toxicodendron, Yedra, 195
Ristra, see Chile, Maíz
Rocky mountain bee plant, Guaco, 93
Rocky mountain sage, Estafiate, 82
ROMERILLO, *Artemisia filifolia,* 171
(also Escoba de la víbora, 80)
ROMERILLO DEL LLANO, 172
ROMERO DE CASTILLA, *Chrysanthemum balsamita,* 172
(also Punche, 165)
Rosaceae, see Palo duro, Rosa cimarron
ROSA CIMARRON, *Rosa fendleri,* 172
ROSA DE CASTILLA, *Rosa,* 173, 174

269

ROSA DEL CAMPO, Rosa fendleri, 172

Rosa fendleri, Rosa cimarron, 172

Rose family, see Rosaceae

ROSETA, *Cenchrus pauciflorus,* 175

Rosetilla, Yerba del sapo, 212

ROSITA MORADA, *Phlox nana,* 175

RUDA, *Ruta graveolens,* 176

RUDA CIMARRON, *Thalictrum fendleri,* 177

RUDA DE LA SIERRA, *Thalictrum fendleri,* 177

Rudbeckia laciniata, Dormilón, 74

Rudbeckia tagetes, Dormilón, 74

Rue, Ruda, 176

Rue family, see Rutaceae

Rum cherry, Capulín, 51

Rumex, Lengua de vaca, 113

Rumex crispus, Lengua de vaaca, 113

Rumex hymenosephalus, Caña agria, 47

Ruta graveolens, Ruda, 176

Rutaceae, see Ruda

SABINA MACHO, *Juniperus sibirica,* 178

Sacatón, Popotón, 163

Safflower, Azafrán, 37

Saffron, Azafrán, 37

Sagebrush, Anisote, 37; Chamiso hediondo, 57; Mariola, 128

Saint Peter's wort, Altimisa mexicana, 31

Saitas, Cebollita del campo, 55

Salicaceae, see Álamo de hoja redonda, Álamo sauco, Jarita

Salix exigua, Jarita, 104

Salt, use of, see Aceite de la víbora, Altamisa de la sierra, Añil del muerto, Anisote, Brazíl, Cadillos, Chamiso, Chan, Chile, Coronilla, Cuipa de sabina, Geranio, Higos, Malva, Pazote, Poléo, Poléo del pais, Póñil, Ponso, Popotón, Romerillo, Tomate del campo, Tomatillo del campo, Trementina de piñon, Yedra, Yerba de la quintana, Yerba del sapo

Saltbush, Chamiso, 56

Salts of sorrel, Socoyol, 180

Salvia reflexa, Chan, 59

Sambuscus melanocarpa, Flor de sauz, 86

Sambuscus mexicana, Flor de sauz, 86

San Ildefonso Indians, see Chicória, Contrayerba, Maíz, Guaco, Orégano, Palmilla, Póñil

San Juan Indians, see Agua piedra

Sanalotodo, see Trementina de piñon, 192

Sand bur, see Roseta, 175

Sand berbena, Lechuguilla, 111

Sandbar willow, Jarita, 104

SANGRE (Blood), 178

Sangre de Cristo, Yerba de la sangre, 201

SANGRE DE VENADO, *Calamus draco,* 179
(also see Azahar, 179; Brazíl, 41; Póñil, 161)

Santa Clara Indians, see Ajo, Chicória, Maíz, Orégano, Palmilla, Rosa cimarron

Santo Domingo Indians, see Cadillos, Leche de conejo, Toloache, Yerba de la piedra, Yerba sin raiz

Santivalia aberti, Yerba fria, 214

Saponaria officinalis, Clavelina, 66

Saururaceae, see Yerba mansa

Scabbish, Flor de San Juan, 84

Scarlet bugler, Varas de San José, 194

Scarlet gaura, Yerba de la Virgen, 202

Scouring rush, Cañutillo del llano, 51

Screw bean, Tornillo, 190

Scrophulariaceae, see Flor de Santa Rita, Punchón, Varas de San José, Yerba del apache

Scurvish, Flor de San Juan, 84

Sedum, sp. Siempreviva, 180

Senecio ambrosioides, Yerba del caballo, 205

Senecio filifolius, Yerba del caballo, 205

Senecio multicapitatus, Yerba del caballo, 205

Shad scale, Chamiso, 56

Shamrock, Socoyol, 180

Sheep skin, use of, see Cal, Caña agria

Sheep weed, Escoba de la víbora, 80

SIEMPREVIA, *Sedum* sp., 180

Silenaceae, see Clavelina

Silver nitrate, Piedra infernal, 153

Silver sage, Romerillo, 171

Sioux Indians, see Maíz

Skunk lard, Manteca de zorillo, 123

Skunk bush, Lemita, 112

Sleepy grass, Popotón, 163

Snakeweed, Escoba de la víbora, 80

Sneezeweed, Plumajillo, 158

Soap root, Palmilla, 143

Soap substitute, see Clavelina, Calabazilla, Yucca

Soapweed, Palmilla, 143

Soapwort, Clavelina, 66

SOCOYOL, *Oxalis violaceae,* 180

Soda, see Cuipa de sabina, 72

Sodium bicarbonate, see Tequesquite, 182

REMEDY INDEX

●

ABSCESS, see Yerba de la quintana, 201
"ACHING BONES," see Yerba del caballo, 205
ALTERATIVE, see Yerba de la sangre, 201; Yerba del peco, 210
ANAEMIA, see Coralillo, 68; Coronilla, 69; Encinillo, 78; Guaco, 93, Yerba de la sangre, 201
ANODYNE, see Inmortal, 36; Moradilla, 131; Toloache, 185; Yerba del lobo, 207; Yerba del peco, 210
ANTHELMINTIC, see Estafiate, 82
ANTIBLENNORRHAGIC, see Cañutillo del campo, 49
ANTILUETIC, see Cañutillo del campo, 49; Yerba mansa, 215
ANTISCORBUTIC, see Berro, 40
ANTISPASMODIC, see Maíz, 116
APPENDICITIS, see Pazote, 150
AROMATIC, see Culantro, 73
ARTHRITIS, see Cañutillo del campo, 49
ASTHMA, see Durazno, 76; Estafiate, 82; Higos, 98; Inmortal, 36; Maíz, 116; Punchón, 166; Romerillo, 171; Toloache, 185
ASTRINGENT, see Brazíl, 41; Coralillo, 68; Lengua de vaca, 113; Romerillo, 171; Tornillo, 190

BACKACHE, see Siempreviva, 180
BASKET FIBRE, see Aguapá, 16; Lemita, 112; Yucca, 143

BEVERAGES, see Chicória, 60; Chimajá, 65; Coralillo, 68; Cota, 70; Lemita, 112; Pitajaya, 157; Tornillo, 190
BILIOUSNESS, see Romerillo, 171
BLADDER TROUBLE, see Ajo, 17; Yerba del buey, 203
BLEACHES, see Chile puerco, 65; Pino real colorado, 154
BLEEDING, see Cal, 43
BLEEDING DYSENTERY, see Yerba mansa, 215
BLISTERS, see Yerba del buey, 203
BLOOD IN URINE, see Maíz, 116
BLOOD POISONING, see Cuajo, 71
BLOOD PURIFYER, see Álamo sauco, 21; Cañutillo del campo, 49; Capulín, 51; Chicória, 60; Chile, 62; Cota, 70; Encinillo, 78; Manzanilla, 123; Yerba de la sangre, 201; Yerba del lobo, 207, Yerba mansa, 215; Zarza, 218
BOILS, see Álamo de hoja redonda, 19; Azafrán, 37; Linasa, 114; Malva de castilla, 122; Tecomaca, 181; Toloache, 185
BONE FRACTURE, see Álamo de hoja redonda, 19; Cardo santo, 52, 53; Chicória, 60; Plumajillo, 158; Yerba de la negrita, 199
BOWEL PAINS, see Ajo, 17
BRAIN REMEDY, see Chile, 62
BRONCHITIS, see Añil, 33; Flor de sauz, 86; Manzanilla, 123

275

BRUISES, see Chicória, 60; Hediondilla, 96; Malva de castilla, 122; Oshá, 139; Plumajillo, 158
BURNS, see Cal, 43; Yerba mansa, 215; Yerba del buey, 203
BULLET WOUNDS, see Maíz, 116

CANCER, see Áñil del muerto, 35; Encino, 78
CANKER SORES, see Hormigas meliferas, 102
CARMINATIVE, see Anís, 36; Azafrán, 37; Culantro, 73
CATAMENIA, see Hinojo, 99; Manzanilla, 123; Pazote, 150
CATAPLASM, see Malva, 121
CATARACT IN EYE, see Piedra lumbre, 153
CATARRH, see Inmortal, 36; Poléo, 159; Tomatillo del campo, 188
CEMENT, see Hediondilla, 96
CHEWING GUM, see Almáciga de sabina, 29; Chicote embarrañada, 61; Lechones, 109; Lechuguilla, 111; Lemita, 112; Pinhué, 154; Piñon, 155
CHICKEN CURE, see Escoba de la víbora, 80; Sangre, 178
CHILBLAINS, see Cebolla, 54; Marrubio, 129
CHILDBIRTH, see Albáca, 21; Alhucema, 28; Amolillo, 31; Azafrán, 37; Bellota de sabina, 40; Chile, 62; Frijoles, 89; Hediondilla, 96; Hinojo, 99; Inmortal, 36; Leche de vaca, 108; Malva 121; Malva de castilla, 122; Manzanilla ,123; Mariola, 128; Pamiliia, 143; Pazote, 150; Poléo, 159; Punche, 165; Rama de sabina, 169; Yerbabuena, 195
CHILDREN UNABLE TO WALK, see Hormigas coloradas, 101
CHILLS, see Ponso, 163
CLABBER, see Tomatillo del campo, 188
CLOTTED BLOOD, see Amolillo, 31
COLD, see Albáca, 21; Alcanfor, 23; Amores, 32; Cañutillo del campo, 49; Cebadilla, 53; Cebolla, 54; Chamiso hediondo, 56; Coronilla, 69; Culantro, 73; Flor de sauz, 86; Manteca de zorillo, 123; Manzanilla, 123; Mostaza, 131; Poléo, 159; Poléo chino, 160; Punche, 165; Toloache, 185; Varas de San José, 194; Yerba del buey, 203
"COLD IN THE BONES," see Yerba del buey, 203

"COLD IN THE LUNGS," see Habas, 95
"COLD IN THE RIBS," see Inmortal, 36
"COLD IN THE STOMACH," see Bellota de sabina, 40; Culantro, 73; Yerba del chivatito, 206
COLIC, see Albáca, 21; Alhucema, 28; Altamisa del la sierra, 29; Anís, 36; Anisote, 37; Chan, 59; Estafiate, 82; Manzanilla, 123; Oshá, 139; Punche, 165; Ruda de la sierra, 177; Sabina macho, 178; Yerba del lobo, 207; Yerba del zorillo, 214; Yerba mansa, 215
COMPLEXION BALMS, see skin troubles
CONSUMPTION, see Marrubio, 129; Oshá, 139
CORNS, see Clavelina, 66; Siempreviva, 180
CORPSE CURE, see The Efficacious Dead, 182
COUGH, see Cebolla, 54; Estafiate, 82; Malva de castilla, 122; Maíz, 116; Marrubio, 129; Orégano, 138; Plumajillo, 158; Póñil, 161; Teconblate, 181; Yerba de coriz, 197
COUGHDROPS, see Oshá, 139
CROUP, see Manteca de zorillo, 123
CUTS, see Cadillos, 42; Oshá, 139; Piñon, 155; Plumajillo, 158; Yerba mansa, 215

DEAFNESS, see Ruda, 176
DEMULCENT, see Malva, 121
DIAPHORETIC, see Berro, 40; Maíz, 116; Ponso, 163
DIARRHEA, see Albáca, 21; Altamisa de la sierra, 29; Cadillos, 42; Cardo santo, 52; Chile, 62; Contra yerba, 67; Encino, 78; Estafiate, 82; Hormigas coloradas, 101; Pagué, 142; Palmilla, 143; Patita de león, 148; Toloache, 185; Yerbabuena, 195; Yerba del lobo, 207; Yerba del peco, 210; Yerba mansa, 215
DIPTHERIA, see Yerba del oso, 209; Ajo, 17
DISTENDED STOMACH, see Tequesquite, 182
DIURETIC, see Alfilerillo, 27; Barbasco, 38; Cañutillo del campo, 49; Cota, 70; Dormilón, 74; Entraña, 79; Flor de Santa Rita, 85: Maíz, 116; Yerba de la sangre, 201; Yerba del negro, 208
DOUCHE, see Durazno, 76; Oshá, 139

DROOLING INFANTS, see Chamiso cimarron, 57
DROPSY, see Alamo de hoja redonda, 19; Añil del muerto, 35; Estiercol de cabra, 56; Cardo santo, 52; Chamiso hediondo, 56; Maravilla, 125; Pitajaya, 157; Zarza, 218.
DRUM MATERIAL, see Alamo de hoja redonda, 19
DRYNESS OF THE NOSE, see Albaricoque, 23
DYSENTERY, see Chile, 62; Contra yerba, 67; Estafiate, 82; Hediondilla, 96; Hormigas coloradas, 101; Patita de león, 148; Pazote, 150; Yerba mansa, 215

EARACHE, see Ajo, 17; Albáca, 21; Barbasco, 38; Cardo santo, 52; Geranio, 92; Manzanilla, 123; Punche, 165; Siempreviva, 180
EARDRUMS, see Hongos, 100
ECZEMA, see Rosa cimarron, 172
EMMENAGOGUE, see Albáca, 21; Amolillo, 31; Calabaza, 45; Dormilón, 75; Estafiate, 82; Hinojo, 99, Malva, 121; Pazote, 150; Poléo chino, 160; Ponso, 163
ENEMA, see Malva de castilla, 122; Oshá, 139
EPILEPSY, see Bellota de sabina, 40
EXPECTORANT, see Durazno, 76; Gordo lobo, 166
EYE WASH, see Hinojo, 99; Leche de vaca, 108; Malva de castilla, 122; Manzanilla, 123; Ruda de la sierra, 177; Tornillo, 190

FALSE COURAGE, see Marihuana, 127
FEBRIFUGE, see Azafrán, 37; Cañutillo del campo, 49; Cebadilla, 53; Cebollita del campo, 55; Chamiso cimarron, 57; Chamiso hediondo, 56; Cota, 70; Durazno, 76; Flor de sauz, 86; Inmortal, 36; Jarita, 104; Laurel, 106; Malva, 121; Manzanilla, 123; Marrubio, 129; Orégano, 138; Oshá, 139; Palo amarillo, 146; Plumajillo, 158; Poléo, 159; Poléo del pais, 161; Ponso, 163; Rosa de castilla, 174; Sabina macho, 178; Yerba del lobo, 207; Yerba del oso, 209; Yerba sin raiz, 216
FENCE POSTS, see Piñon, 155; Tornillo, 190
FEVER BLISTERS, see Rosita morada, 175

FIRE STICK, see Añil, 33
FIREWOOD, see Pino real colorado, 154; Piñon, 155
FITS, see Punche, 165; Sangre, 178
FLATULENCY, see Ajo, 17; Cebollita del campo, 55; Chamiso hediondo, 55; Remolino, 170; Romerillo, 171
FLAVORING, see Ajo, 17; Añis, 36; Azafrán, 37; Chico, 59; Chimajá, 65; Culantro, 73; Geranio, 92; Hinojo, 99; Laurel, 106; Lecheros, 109; Orégano, 138; Orégano del campo, 139; Oshá, 139; Poléo del pais, 161, Yerbabuena, 195
"FLU," see Chamiso hediondo, 56; Oshá, 139
FODDER, see Añil, 33; Chico, 59; Chile puerco, 65; Entraña, 79; Nopal, 133; Paja, 142; Tornillo, 190
FONTANEL, see Manzanilla, 123
FOOD, see Aguapá, 16; Albaricoque, 23; Alfalfa, 26; Añil, 33; Bellota de sabina, 40; Cal, 43; Cebollita del campo, 53; Chico, 59; Chicória, 60; Chile, 62; Chile puerco, 65; Durazno, 76; Frijoles, 89; Guaco, 93; Lecheros, 109; Lechones, 109; Lemita, 112; Lengua de vaca, 113; Lirio, 115; Maíz, 116; Malva de castilla, 122; Palmilla, 143; Papa cimarron, 148; Piñon, 155; Pitajaya, 157; Quelite salado, 168; Quelites yus, 169; Socoyol, 180; Teconblate, 181; Tomatito, 190; Tornillo, 190; Yerbabuena, 195
FOREIGN SUBTANCE IN EYE, see Chan, 59; Frijoles, 89
FRECKLES, see Flor de San Juan, 84; Higos, 98; Lechones, 109
FROZEN FEET, see Marrubio, 129
FUMIGANT, see Alhucema, 28; Chile, 62; Yerba sin raiz, 216 (also see Insecticides)

GARGLE, see Caña agria, 47; Tornillo, 190; Yerba del caballo, 205
GOITRE, see Albaricoque, 23; Maravilla, 125; The Efficacious Dead, 182
GOLPES, see Yerba de San Pedro
GONORRHEA, see Alfilerillo, 27; Cañutillo del campo, 49; Coralillo, 68; Dormilón, 74; Manzanilla, 123; Palmilla, 143
GREASE SPOT REMOVER, see Calabazilla, 45

GUM, see Chewing gum
"GREENS," see Food

HAIR DYE, see Marrubio, 129
HAIR TONIC, see Azafrán, 37; Calabazilla, 45; Entraña, 79; Lemita, 112; Manzanilla, 123; Palmilla, 143; Trigo, 193; Yerba de la negrita, 199
HALITOSIS, see Yerba del pescado, 211
HEADACHE, see Alcanfor, 23; Barbasco, 38; Cebadilla, 53; Cornonilla, 69; Culantro, 73; Frijoles, 89; Geranio, 92; Inmortal, 36; Lantén, 106; Laurel, 106; Lengua de vaca, 113; Malva, 121; Orégano, 138; Oshá, 139; Papas, 148; Patito del pais, 149; Poléo, 159; Ruda, 176; Ruda de la sierra, 177; Tecomaca, 181; Tomatillo del campo, 188; Trementina de piñon, 192; Yerba de la negrita, 199; Yerba de la piedra, 200
HEART TROUBLE, see Alegría, 24; Azafrán, 37; Berro, 40; Brazíl, 41; Chile, 62; Chicória, 60; Hinojo, 99; Inmortal, 36; Maíz, 116; Rosa de castilla, 173; Tequesquite, 182
HEMORRHAGE, see Patita de león, 148; Romero de castilla, 172
HEMORRHOIDS, see Higos, 98
HEMOSTATIC, see Chamiso hediondo, 56
HONEY, see Flor de Santa Rita, 85; Patitos, 193
HYPNOTIC, see Toloache, 185

INSECTICIDE, see Ajo, 17; Albáca, 21; Alfalfa, 26; Alfalfón, 26; Barbasco, 38; Calabazilla, 45; Cebadilla, 53; Chan, 59; Chile, 62; Guaco, 93; Hormigas coloradas, 101; Leche de conejo, 107; Manteca de zorillo, 123; Oshá, 139; Palo duro, 147; Punche, 165; Queso, 169; Toloache, 185; Yerba sin raiz, 216
INTESTINAL ANTISPASMODIC, see Maíz, 116; Rama de sabina, 169; Tornillo, 190
INTESTINAL DIFFICULTIES, see, Aceite mexicano, 15; Estafiate, 82; Guaco, 93; Hediondilla, 96

JAUNDICE, see Alegría, 24; Brazíl, 41; Cebolla, 54; Duranzo, 76; Punche, 165; Yerba sin raiz, 216
JELLY, see Lemita, 112, Nopal, 133
"JUEGOS EN LA BOCA," (Sores in the mouth), see Habas, 95
"JUMPING STOMACH," see Yerba del sapo, 212

KIDNEY TROUBLE, see Agua piedra, 16; Ajo, 17; Berro, 40; Cañutillo del campo, 49; Chile, 62; Flor de San Juan, 84; Hediondilla, 96; Hormigas coloradas, 101; Hueso de cereza, 103; Popotón, 163; Punche, 165; Varas de San José, 194; Yerba del buey, 203; Zarzilla, 219

LACTATION, see Lecheros, 108; Lechones, 109; Lechuguilla, 111; Roseta, 175; Yerba de la golondrina, 198
LASTIMADO, see Yerba de la Piedra, 200
LAXATIVE, see Altamisa de la sierra, 29; Calabazilla, 45; Higos, 98; Malva, 121; Palo duro, 147; Yerba de la sangre, 201; (See also Purge)
LEPROSY, see Flor de Santa Rita, 85; Moradilla, 131; Musgo, 132; Yerba del lobo, 207
LIGHTNING PROTECTOR, see Palo amarillo, 146
LIVER SPOTS, see Pino real colorado, 154
LOCOED HORSE, see Calabazilla, 45; Frijolillo, 90
LOOSE TEETH, see Yerba del oso, 209
LOVE CHARM, see Plumajillo, 158; Sangre de venado, 179; Toloache, 185; Yerba sin raiz, 216
LUNG INFECTIONS, see Añil, 33; Chile, 62; Punchón, 166; Yerba del buey, 203

MAD-DOG BITE, see Poléo del pais, 161
MALARIA, see Encino, 78; Escoba de la víbora, 80; Palo amarillo, 146
MEASELS, see Azafrán, 37; Higos, 98; Malva de castilla, 122

MENOSTATIC, see Altamisa mexi-
cana, 31; Añil del muerto, 35; Es-
coba de la víbora, 80
MENSTRUATION, see Cuero, 71;
Dormilón, 75; Durazno, 76; Maíz,
116; Manzanilla, 123; Poléo, 159;
Remolino, 170; Tornillo, 190; Va-
ras de San José, 194, Yerba de la
sangre, 201; Yerba del sapo, 212;
Yerba del zorillo, 214
MOLLERA (fontanel), see Manzan-
illa, 123
MUMPS, see Linasa, 114; Nopal, 133,
Patito del pais, 149

NARCOTIC, see Marihuana, 127;
Popotón, 163; Toloache, 185
NEURALGIA, see Anís, 36; Barbasco, 38; Cebadilla, 53; Laurel, 106;
Manzanilla, 123; Ruda, 176; Sangre de venado, 179; Tecomaca,
181; Yerbabuena, 195; Yerba del
peco, 210
NOSEBLEED, see Lama del agua,
105; Piedra lumbre, 153

OIL, see Añil, 35; Cadillos, 42; Geranio, 92; Hinojo, 99; Marrubio,
129; Pino real colorado, 154; Rosa
cimarron, 1172
OINTMENT, see Azafrán, 37; Trementina de piñon, 192; Yerba
mansa, 215
OVEREATING, see Maravilla, 125

PAINS, see Alcanfor, 23; Lechones,
109; Yerba de San Pedro, 197;
Yerba del apache, 203
PAINS IN THE BACK, see Mora-
dilla, 131; Pegapega, 152; Rosa de
castilla, 173
PAINS IN THE CHEST, see Cha-
miso hediondo, 56; Inmortal, 36
PAINS IN THE FACE, see Le-
chones, 109
PAINS IN THE INTESTINES, see
Aceite mexicano, 15
PAINS IN THE LEG, see Nogal,
132
PAINS IN THE NECK, see Poléo
del pais, 161
PAINS IN THE SHOULDER, see
Yerba del lobo, 207
PAINT, see Guaco, 93
PAINT DRYER, see Azafrán, 37

PARALYSIS, see Barbasco, 38; Cebadilla, 53; Flor de sauz, 86; Mostaza, 131; Sangre de venado, 179;
Yerba del buey, 203; Yerba del
oso, 209; Zarza, 218
PARTURITION, see Childbirth
PEACH LEAF YEAST, see Durazno, 76
PHLEGM, see Alhucema, 28; Estafiate, 82
PHTHISIS, see Yerba sin raiz, 216
PILES, see Añil del muerto, 35; Escoba de la víbora, 80; Punche,
165; Trementina de piñon, 192;
Yerba mansa, 215
PLEURISY, see Añil, 33; Estafiate,
82
PNEUMONIA, see Albáca, 21; Anís,
36; Habas, 95; Maíz, 116; Malva,
121; Marrubio, 129; Oshá, 139;
Yerba del apache, 203; Yerba del
lobo, 207
POISON, see Quelites yus, 169
(also see Rattlesnake bites, Insecticides)
POISON IVY, see Yedra, 195; Yerba
del buey, 203
POISON OAK, see Yerba del buey,
203; Yerba del oso, 209
PURGE, see Amores, 32; Barbasco,
38; Calabazilla, 45; Cebadilla, 53;
Chile, 62; Durazno, 76; Estafiate,
82; Flor de sauz, 86; Malva, 121;
Malva de castilla, 122; Mostaza,
131; Palmilla, 143; Plumajillo,
158; Rosa cimarron, 172; Yerba
del negro, 208
(see also Laxative)
PYORRHEA, see Caña agria, 47;
Culantro, 73; Jarita, 104; Lengua
de vaca, 113; Tierra de rata, 183;
Yerba de la piedra, 200; Yerba
del pescado, 211   1

RABBIT STICK CHARM, see Varas
de San José, 194
RABIES, see Ajo, 17
RAISING BREAD, see Zarza, 218
RATTLESNAKE BITE, see Añil,
33; Cadillos, 42; Escoba de la ví-
bora, 80; Queso, 169
REFRIGERANT, see Yerba fria, 214
RENAL DISORDER, see Cañutillo
del campo, 49
RESOLVENT, see Yerba del peco,
210
RESUSCITATION, see Coronilla, 69
RHEUMATISM, see Aceite de la ví-
bora, 15; Alcanfor, 23; Alfilerillo,
27; Añil del muerto, 35; Calaba-

280

Designed
by
Merle Armitage
Drawings by P. G. Napolitano
Printed by
The Rydal Press
Santa Fe